The Totally Brilliant AMAZING MAZES BOOK

AURA

This edition published in 2016
by Baker & Taylor UK Ltd,
Bicester, Oxfordshire, OX26 4ST

Copyright © Arcturus Holdings Limited
26/27 Bickels Yard, 151–153 Bermondsey Street
London SE1 3HA

ISBN: 978-1-78599-702-0
CH005285NT
Supplier 29, Date 0516, Print run 5222

Compiler: Charlotte Gerlings
Editor: Rebecca Gerlings

Printed in China

CONTENTS

CAT AND FIDDLE

Hey diddle diddle! Chase after the dish
as he runs away with the spoon.

LITTLE MISS MUFFET

Little Miss Muffet doesn't want to share her breakfast with a giant spider! Which way should he go to catch up with her?

LITTLE BO-PEEP

This little shepherdess must follow a winding
path before she finds her flock again.

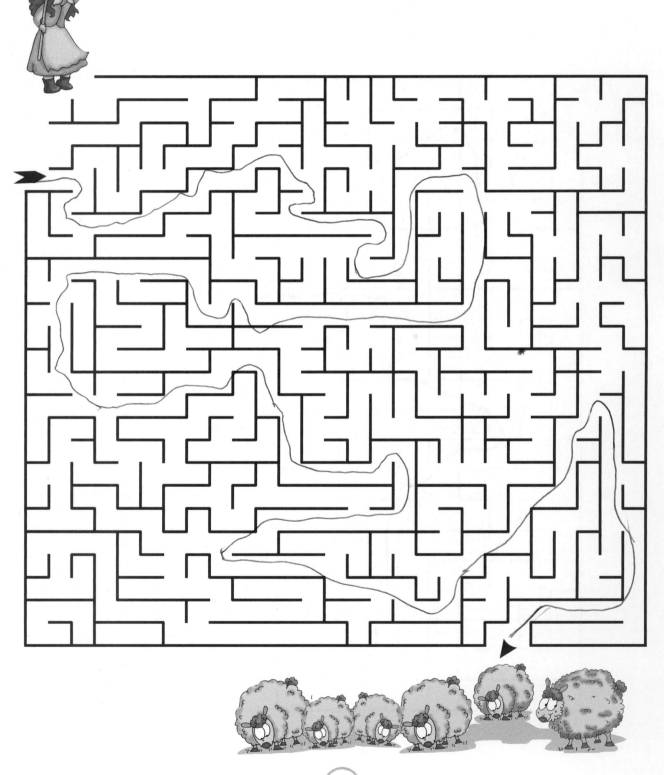

THE KNAVE OF HEARTS

Help Jack escape with the tarts
and avoid meeting the angry Queen!

THREE LITTLE KITTENS

These naughty kittens have lost their mittens.
Can you lead them to where they dropped them?

HANSEL AND GRETEL

The children are lost in the wood until
they discover the gingerbread house.

WEE WILLIE WINKIE

This little boy runs here and there through the town making sure all the children are in bed by eight o'clock.

RIDE A COCKHORSE TO BANBURY CROSS

Follow the crooked road to see the fine lady upon a white horse.

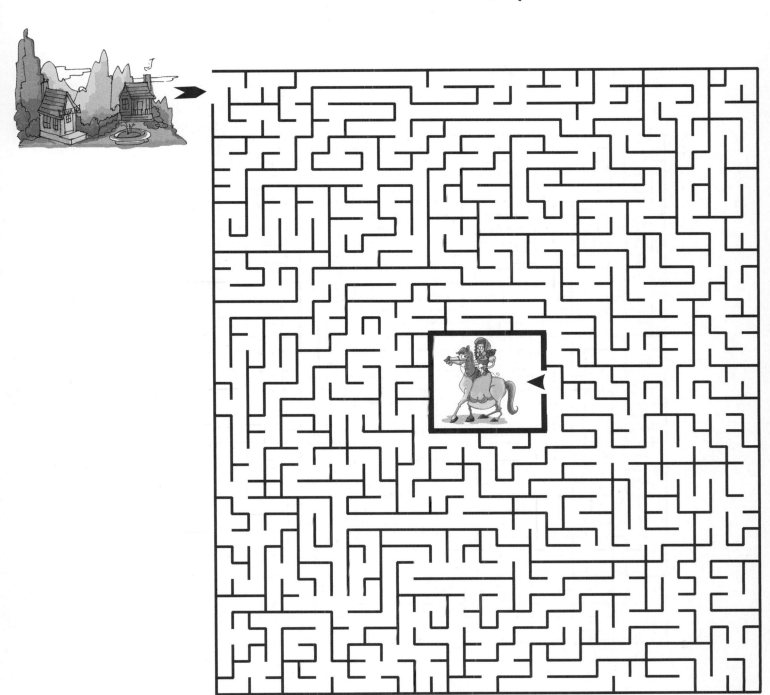

YANKEE DOODLE

He comes to town riding on a pony, but does he get there by the quickest route?

THIS LITTLE PIGGY

This little piggy went to market. Now, which road did he take?

THE PIED PIPER

The musician leads the children away to the magic hillside, but he wanders all over the town first.

HICKORY, DICKORY, DOCK

The mouse ran up the clock, just not in a straight line!

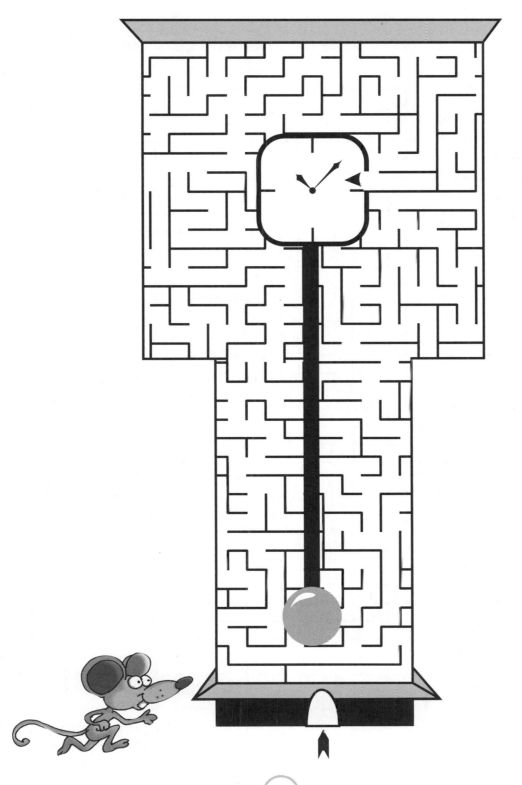

ROBIN HOOD

Robin's camp is hidden in the forest.
Can you find your way to it?

GINGERBREAD MAN

Starting at his hands, follow the lines to reach his buttons.

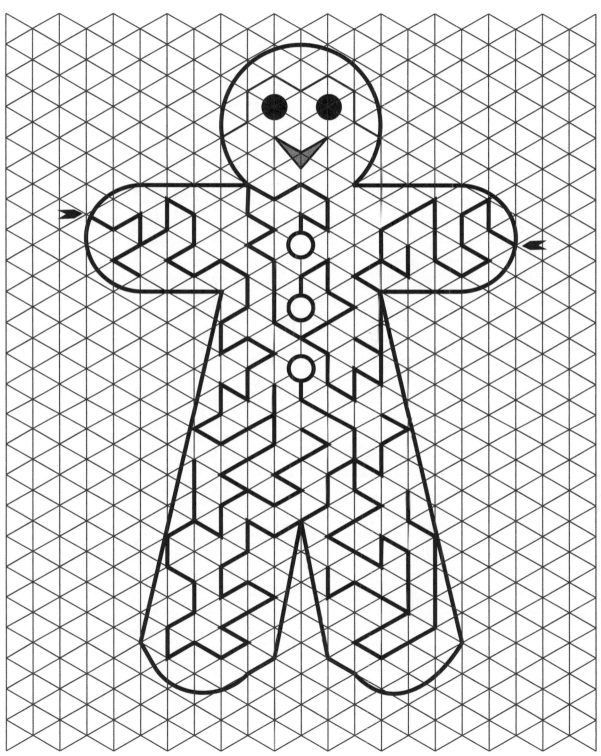

THE GREAT EGGSCAPE

Starting at the top, aim for the gap at the bottom of the shell.

JOURNEY TO THE OASIS

Take this camel to a refreshing drink at the oasis.

BROKEN HEIRLOOM

When the vase shattered, the pieces flew everywhere.
Collect them all so it can be mended.

JACK AND THE BEANSTALK

It's a long way to climb, but there's gold at the top!

KINGFISHER

Down through the rippling water, the kingfisher spies his next meal.

MOUSE AND CHEESE

It doesn't matter where you hide the cheese,
the little mouse will always sniff it out!

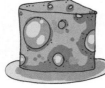

BACK TO THE BAT CAVE

How good is the bat's homing signal?

BUILDING THE PATIO

Hard work, but worth it in the end!

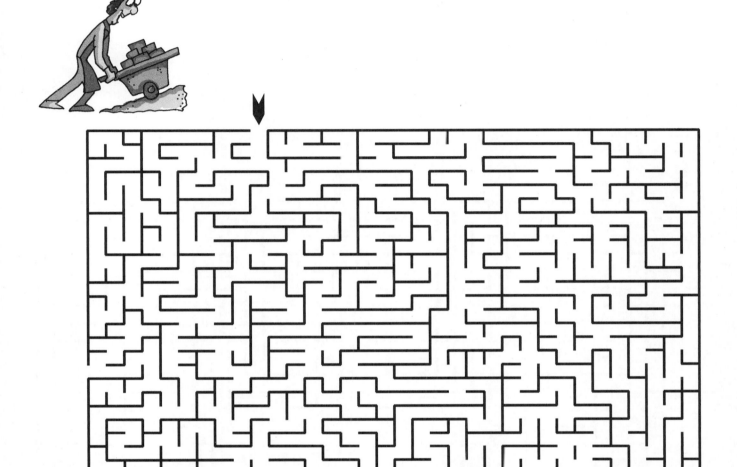

THE SLEEPING BEAUTY.

She lies beyond this maze of briars.
How does the Prince reach her?

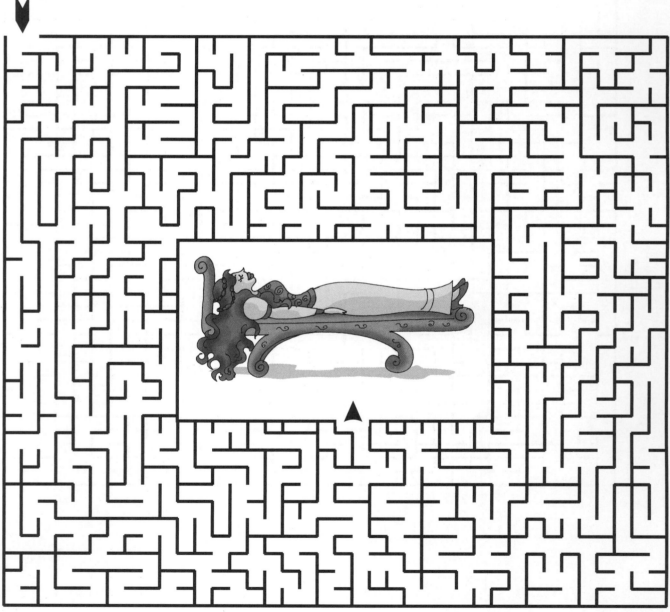

WALK THE CROOKED MILE

Lead the little crooked man home to his little crooked house.

27

THE CROCK OF GOLD

They say it lies at the foot of the rainbow, but this croc
might not be quite what the explorer has in mind...

HOLDING PATTERN

You are piloting an airliner and have to make several detours before you finally reach the airport.

SKATER'S WALTZ

Help Kate skate to victory in the ice dance championship.

HOPSCOTCH

Hop and jump to the end of this puzzle.

HALLOWEEN

Carve a route through this Jack o' Lantern maze.

MERLIN'S HAT

Decorate the wizard's hat as you travel from the brim to the tip.

VALENTINE

Follow the path of Cupid's arrow.

BLOWING BUBBLES

Pretty bubbles in the air!

ANYONE FOR TENNIS?

This could be game, set, and match for someone.

SPIDER'S WEB

Take Sid the spider to lunch!

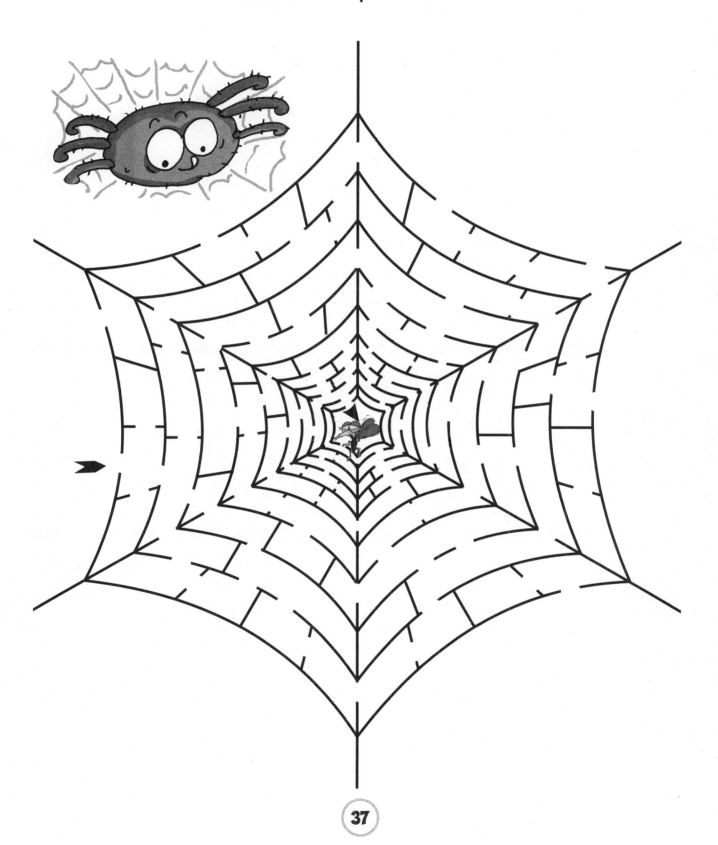

SWIMMING RACE

Kara, Sara, and Tara are getting tired as they swim the final length of the pool. Who swims the straightest line to the finish?

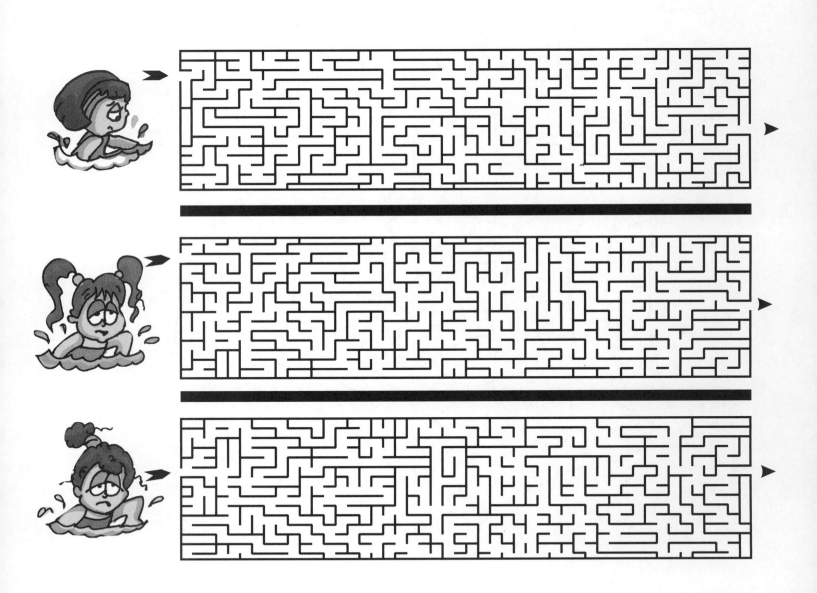

LABYRINTH CHALLENGE

Can you swim through the underwater labyrinth and out the other side?

SKULL AND CROSSBONES

Ahoy there, me hearties! Can you make it to the treasure before Captain Hook gets his hand on it?

JIGMAZE

Can you solve the puzzle of this jigsaw?

DIPLODOCUS

A beast of little brain. See how long it takes to get a message to its tail.

ISLAND HIDEAWAY

You've entered the secret lair of the supervillain!
Can you find your way out?

THE NORTHWEST PASSAGE

Inside the Arctic Circle lies a maze of islands and drifting ice.
Find your own route across the fabled Northwest Passage.

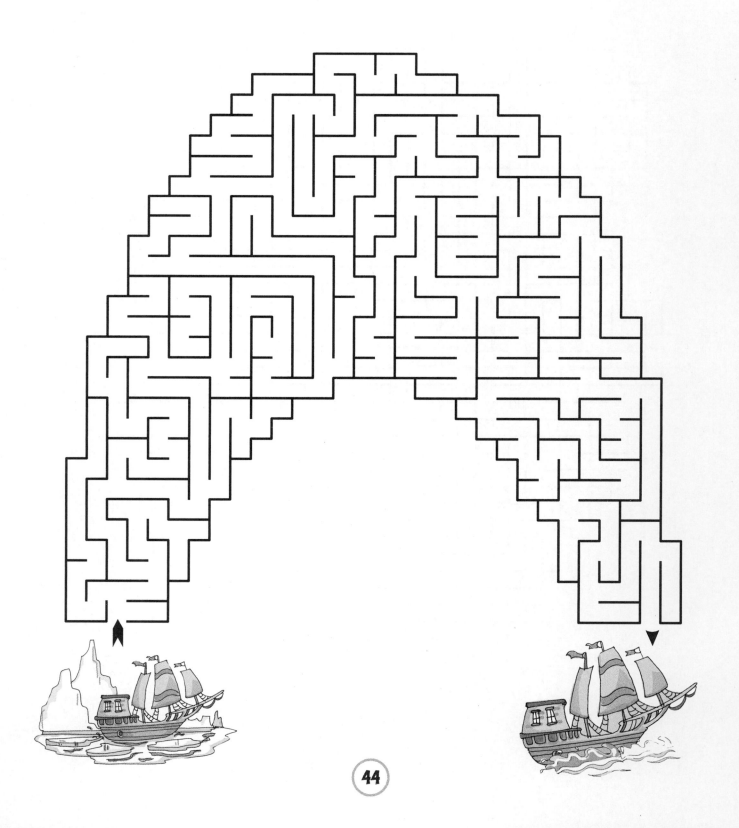

44

CASH CHASE

The bank robber's case has sprung a leak so
the police should have no trouble tracking him down.

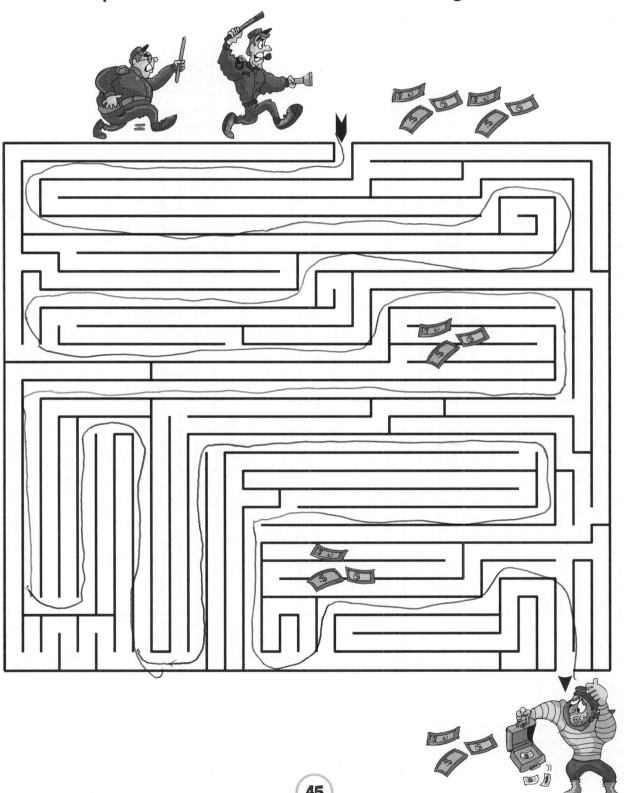

CROSS-CITY MONORAIL

Help this city train call at all six stations on the route.

SQUIRRELS' SAFARI

Squirrels bury their nuts in your lawn for winter food
but never seem to be able to find them again.

PUTTING IN THE PRACTICE

Putt round this putting-green until you exit at the ninth hole.

48

TOBOGGAN RUN

The icy downhill run is swift but full of tricky twists and turns.

FINISH

SHOWJUMP

Jump for joy if you complete this course without any knockdowns or refusals.

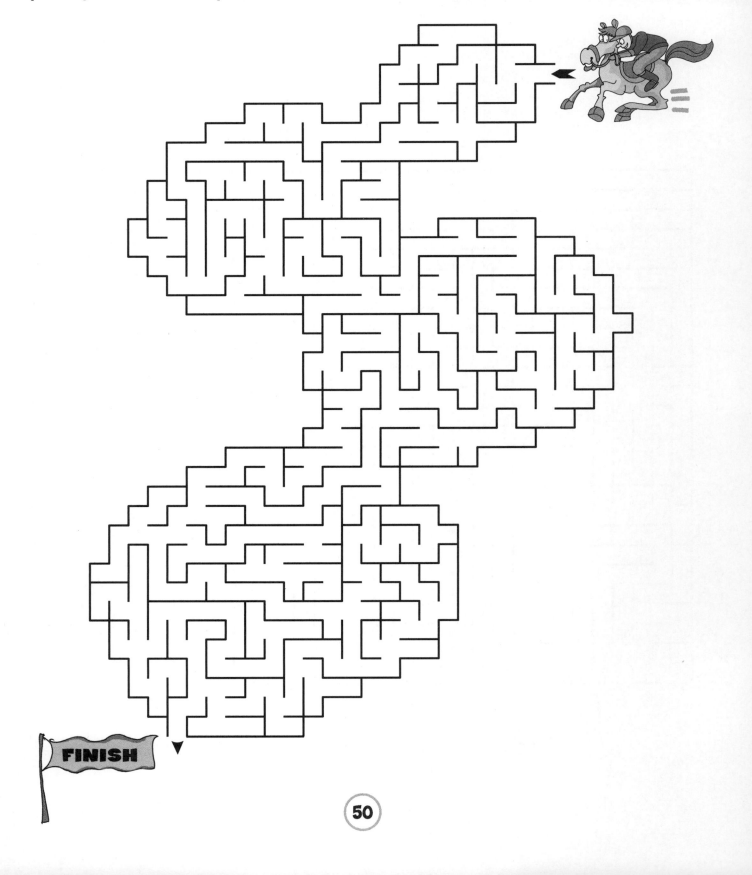

FINISH

50

BY HELICOPTER

The pilot has to land in some dangerous terrain, avoiding the dense jungle and a ravine.

CITY MARATHON

Never underestimate the need for training!

FINISH

MOONSCAPE

Steer the moon buggy from crater to crater and back to the spaceship.

WRECK RECCE

The diver has only limited time to explore the wreck at this depth. Help him find his way down quickly.

SALES SCRUM

The bargains are to be found all over the store,
so rush everywhere to collect them all.

SURF'S UP!

Take this surfer through
the waves to the shore..

MAIZE MAZE

This one's a bit corny!

FIRE RESCUE!

Lead the way and help the firemen complete their rescue operation.

FIND THE GARAGE

This old car needs a lot of fixing! Take it to the garage before it stops completely.

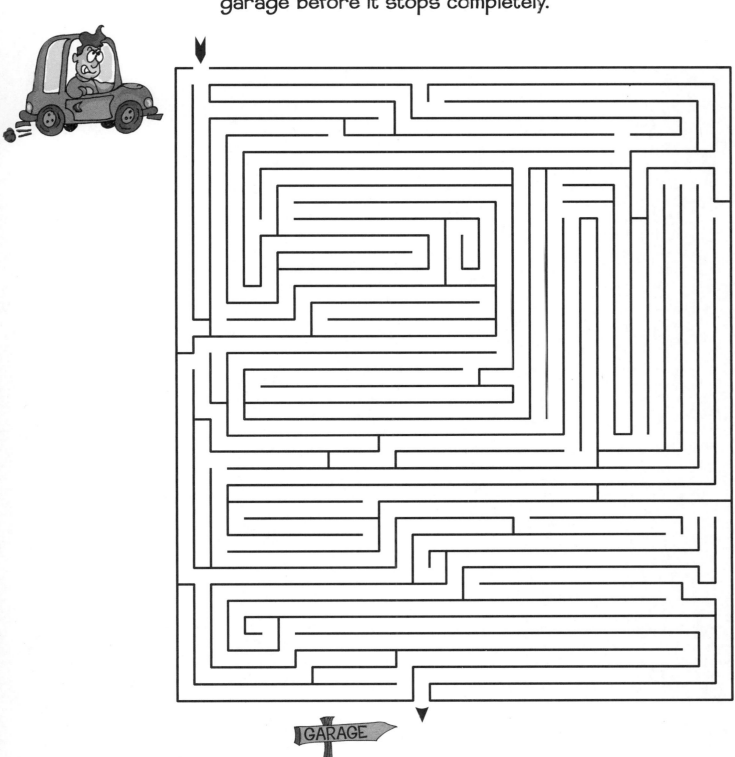

RACE FOR GOLD

Set the stopwatch: four sprinters are going for Olympic gold.
Who will get there first?

PICNIC PESTS

Enjoy the picnic food while avoiding all the pests who seem to want a share!

CINDERELLA

Will Cinderella be home by midnight or will she lose
her way in the maze of palace corridors?

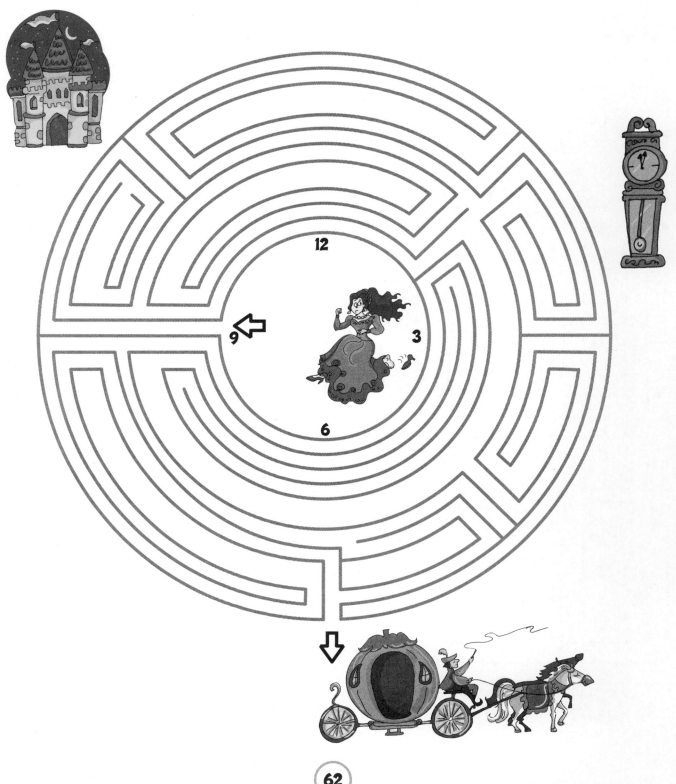

CHOOSING THE CHRISTMAS TREE

The Joneses are going to the plantation to buy their tree.
Can you show them the way?

TOP OF THE TREE

With the star fixed on top of the tree, Christmas festivities can begin.

WHO LET THE DOGS OUT?

Dogs everywhere! You have to round up each one as you go along and take them all back to the kennels in one trip.

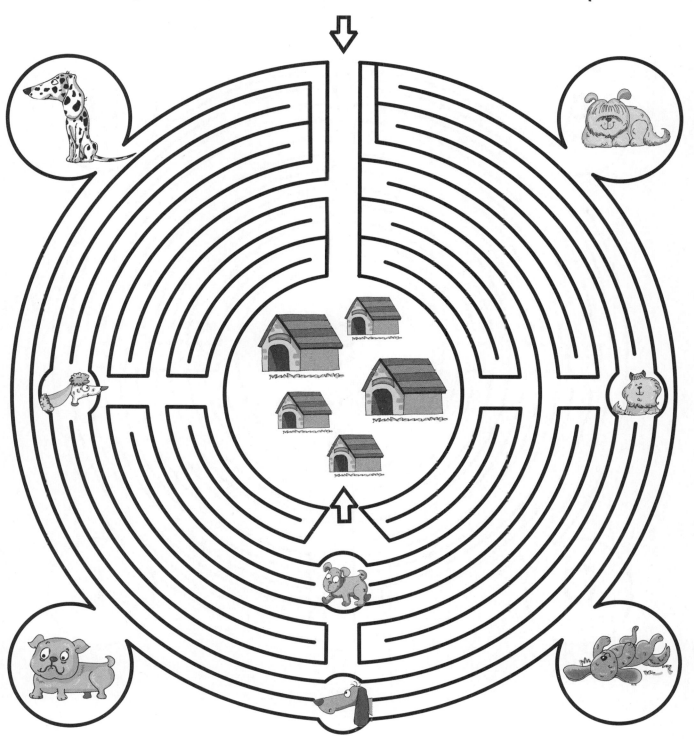

ISLAND IN THE SUN

Start at the middle, picking up the first letter, then carry on around the labyrinth to gather the remaining eight letters. In the correct order, they will spell a famous island.

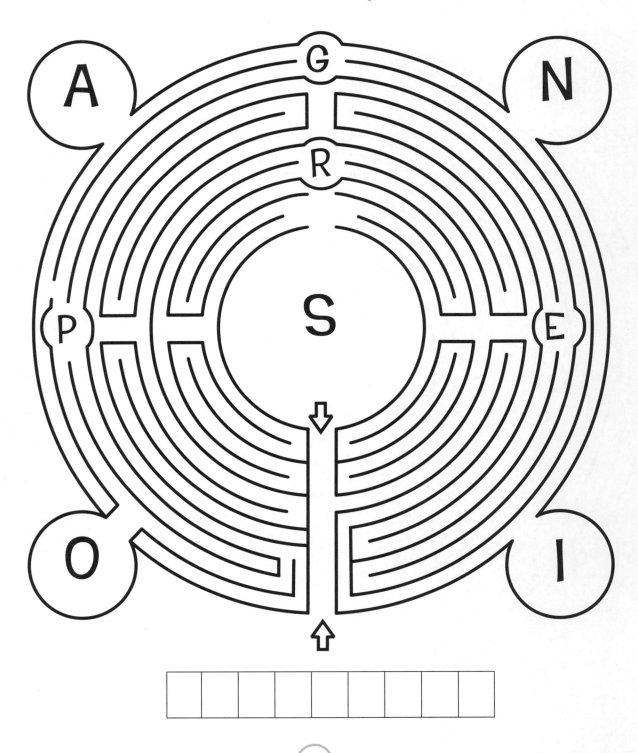

MAGIC STAR

Having recharged her wand with magic stardust, the Good Fairy must now return to earth and make some wishes come true. But which way to go?

ROCK STAR

You're due on stage in 5 minutes. Quick, find your way to your band.

FIND THE FRIENDS

Three girls have become separated in this labyrinth.
One arrow at a time, find the letters of each of their names
in the correct order, and then write them in the boxes.

LOST BOYS

Three boys have lost themselves in this labyrinth.
Following one arrow at a time, find the letters of each of
their names in the correct order, and then write them in the boxes.

DIAMOND QUEST

Go for the jewel in the crown through this diamond maze!

ESCAPE FROM CHACMOOL

Run for your life through this ancient temple to get to the outer wall!

GALLERY GRAB

The alarm has gone off at the city museum, but the guards have to run through a maze of galleries in pursuit of the picture thief.

AS LOVELY AS A ROSE

Guide this bee to the beautiful flower.

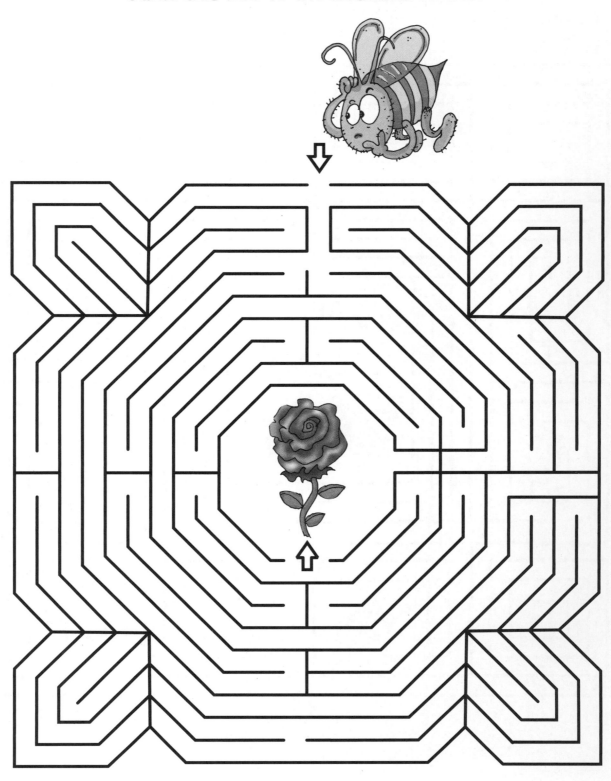

THE MUSIC GOES ROUND AND ROUND

How will the musical notes escape from
this antique gramophone's horn?

IN ONE EAR AND OUT THE OTHER

Mother Bear claims that everything she says to
Baby Bear goes in one ear and out the other.
Trace an unbroken line between his ears to find out if it's true!

BIRTHDAY CAKE

How steady are your hands? Can you make a pattern on this birthday cake in one unbroken line?

THE APPLE TREE

Trace this ancient tree design along the dotted line.

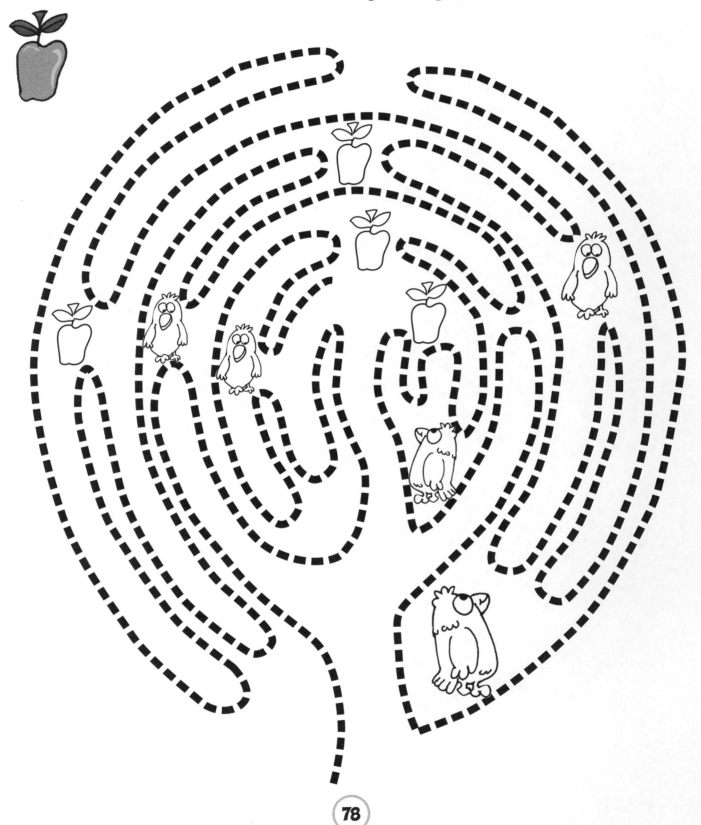

BROKEN BEADS

Grandma's bead necklaces are in a muddle.
How many separate strings are there?

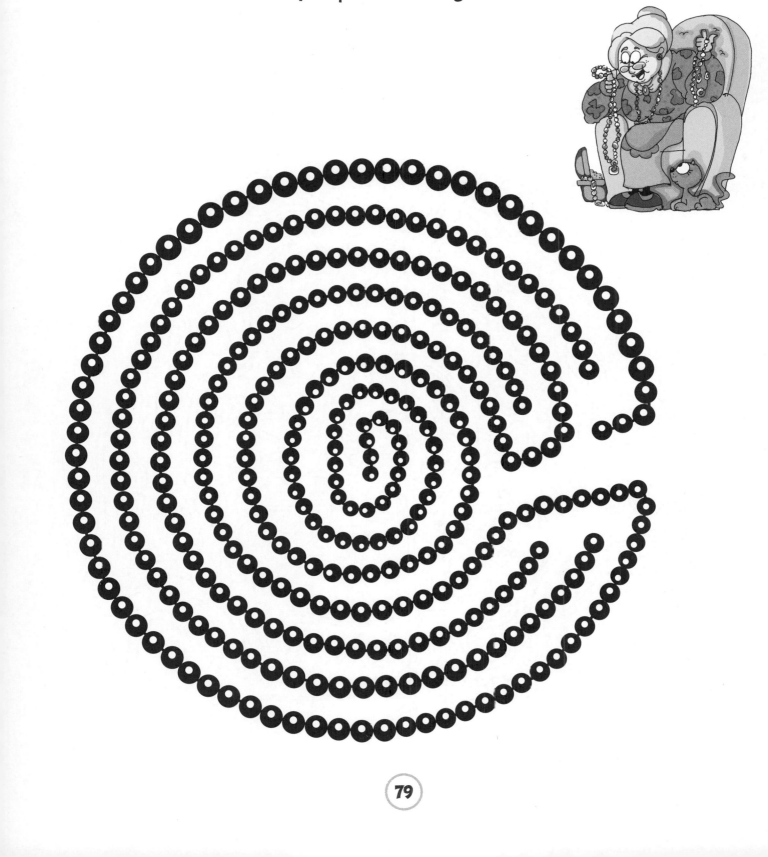

EARLY WORM

It's good to be the early bird but not so good to be the worm!
Can you pick out the tail that connects with his head?

FLYING HIGH

The wind has blown these kites all over the place and tangled their strings. Now, which end belongs to which kite?

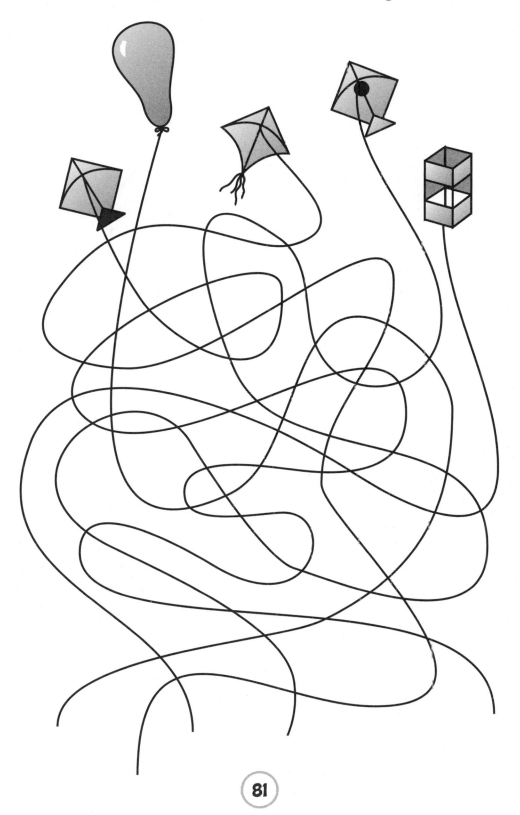

JUMPING ROPES

The children have been told to tidy their toys.
Can you help them to sort out this muddle?

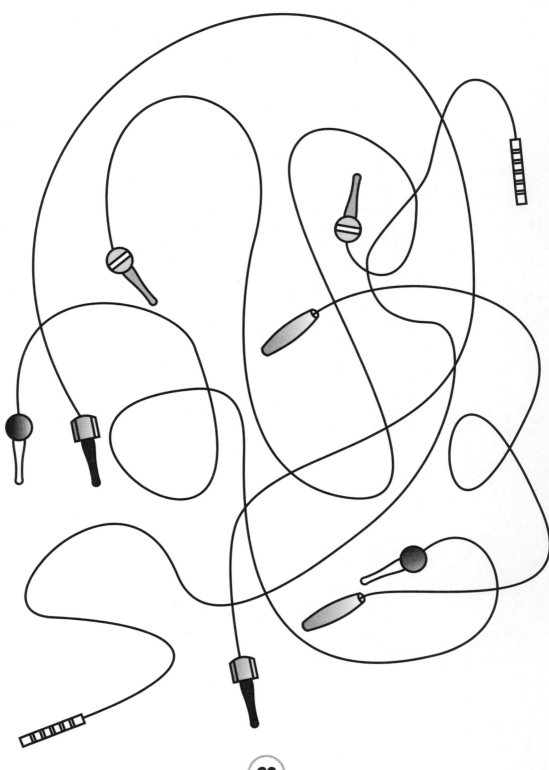

MESSAGE IN A BOTTLE

You've found a bottle with a message inside. Which line should you pull to bring the bottle closer to your boat?

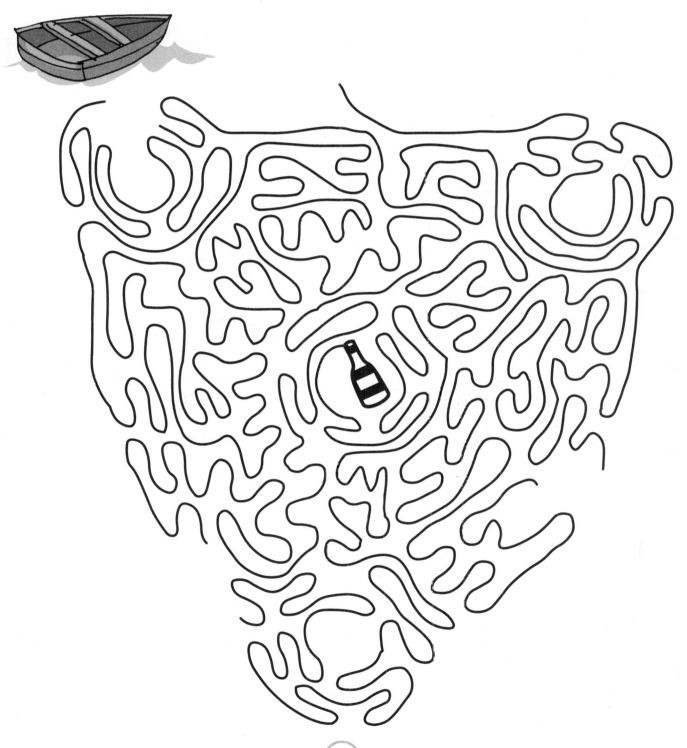

SHOWDOWN

Five finalists walk their dogs around the show ring but, in their excitement, the leads have got crossed. Can you match the dogs to their owners?

KITTY CHAOS

The kittens have upset the knitting circle's workbaskets. Undo this muddle before the ladies discover what they've been up to!

SPAGHETTI

Dan, Joe, and Will decide to share a plate
of spaghetti, but who'll get the most?

SLIPPERY SNAKES

The zookeeper's assistant has got some snakes in a muddle.
Help her separate them before she gets in trouble!

JUMBO JAM

These elephants have stripped the tree bare but none of them will get any dinner until their trunks are unwound!

WHERE'S THE CATCH?

Five fishermen hooked five fish at the same time but the fish have been swimming in circles ever since. Can you untangle the lines?

A STITCH IN TIME

These strands of threads from all these bobbins are in a terrible tangle. Can you get this puzzle sewn up?

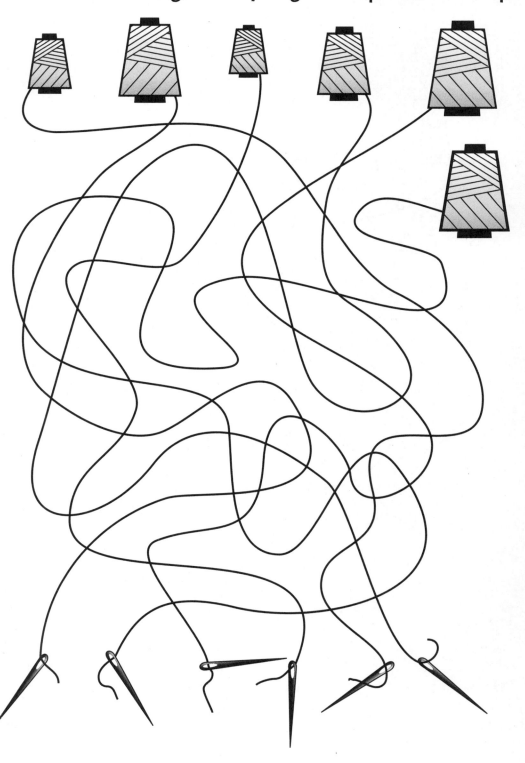

YO-YO, OH NO!

The yo-yo demonstration was going well until someone tried some fancy tricks. Sort out the strings so the demo can begin again.

THAT'S NOT CRICKET

If only these crazy cricketers had looked where they were going! Can you help to disentangle them?

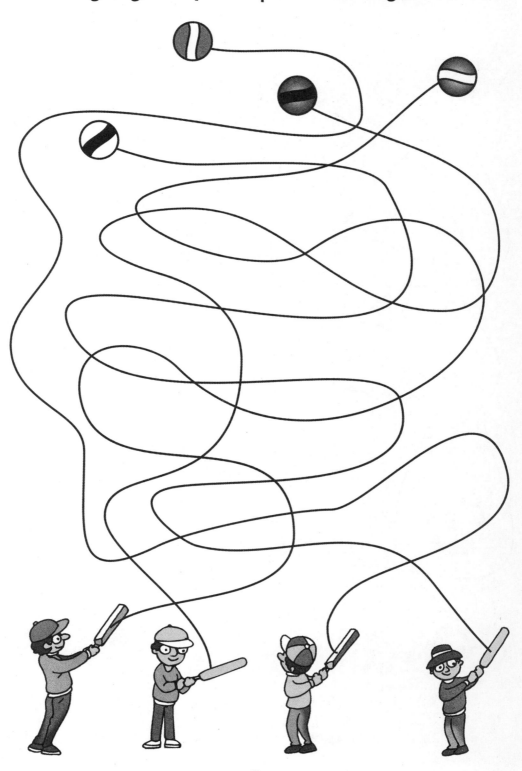

LOST PROPERTY

Someone has left the lost property box in a terrible state.
Five pairs of sports shoes are still joined by their laces,
but is it possible to trace each shoe to its partner?

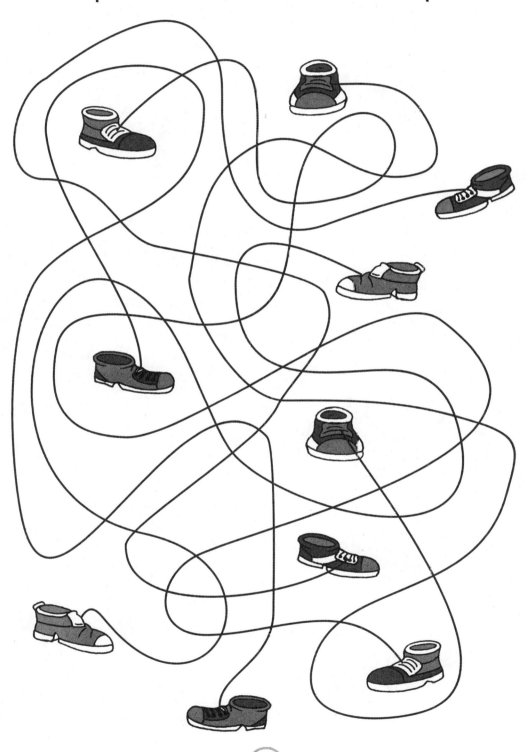

POINT TO POINT

Baylee the ballerina has just sewn ribbons onto
three pairs of ballet shoes in a great hurry. Can you trace
each ribbon to match the shoes?

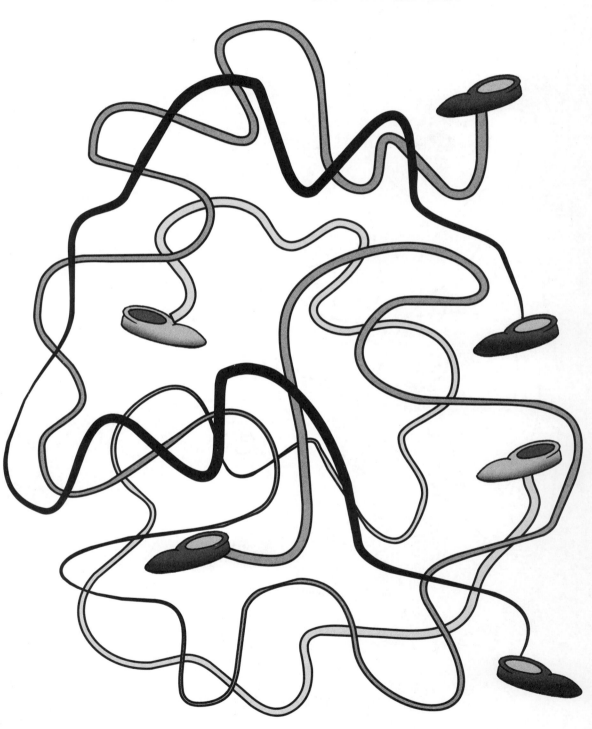

HIGH HOPES

On the way back from the fair these children got the strings of their balloons in a muddle. Can you untangle them before there are tears?

CROOKED PATHS

Whoever built these cottages built crazy paths to go with them.
Trace each path to a separate cottage door.

TRAILING VINES

These grape vines have gone wild.
Trace a path from the plant to the grapes.

SOMETHING FISHY

Each of these fishermen has got a bite, but now their lines have become tangled up. Can you work out whose fish is whose?

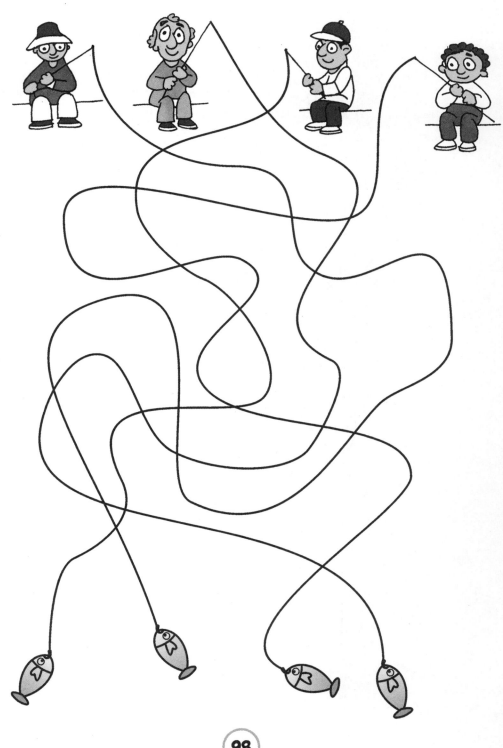

Fractal Mazes

CAT AND MOUSE

Kenny the cat will wait all day. Can Max the mouse find a
way to his safe home in the middle of the maze?

ISLAND RALLY

The rally is about to start, but the road map has been lost. You must draw a new one by tracing the most direct route to the flag.

PRECIPICE

There is only one way up this perilous precipice! Avoid getting stranded on the wrong rocky ledge.

CALL A CAB

Ted has a train to catch. Can the cab driver find his way through this maze of streets to collect him in time?

THE HARE AND THE TORTOISE

Here they go again! Who will find the shortest path to the winning post?

PYRAMID

Which route did the pyramid builders climb to place the final stone on top?

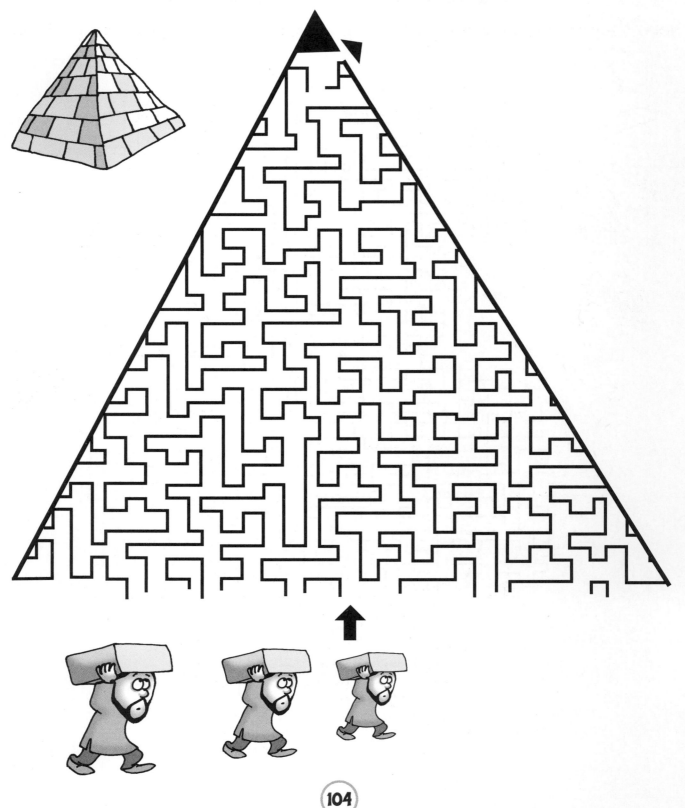

EGGSPECTATION

Draw lines from the dot to a gap in the side of the egg without going over any part of the path more than once. How many fragments of shell does this make?

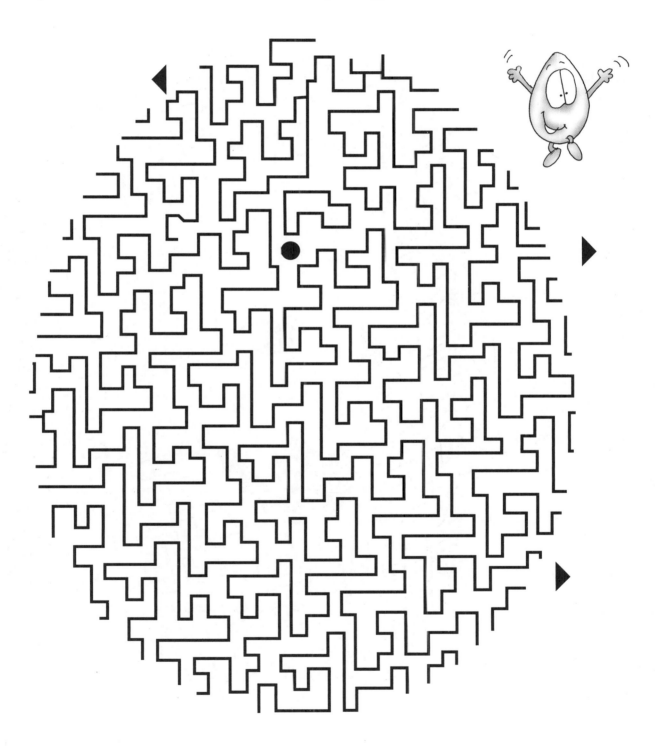

LION

Starting and finishing at the same dot, make your way very carefully right around the lion's mane, avoiding those sharp teeth!

GIRAFFE

Trace a line from top to tail.

WATER TOY

Start at Nessie's neck and find the way to deflate her.

NILE CROCODILE

Trace a line from the crocodile's watchful eye to the tip of his scaly tail.

TORTOISE

Can you follow a clear path through the pattern on his shell?

SEAL

Draw a line that connects the tail of this clever
seal with the ball balanced on his head.

PONY

Saddle the galloping pony if you can.

RHINO

Trace a line from the rhino's ear to his rear.

BABY DEER

Trace a line across the pattern on Bambi's back.

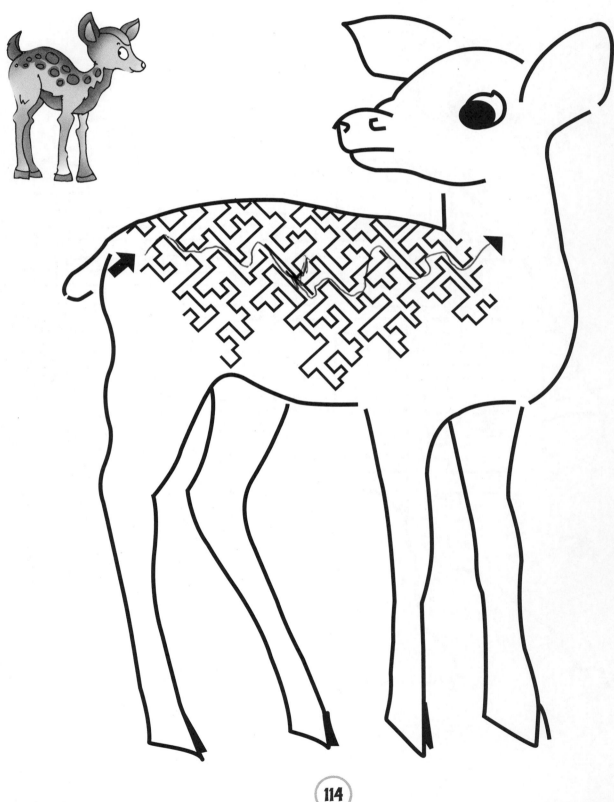

TOADSTOOLS

Make your way through the crazy pattern on these
toxic toadstools and out the other side.

TIGER

Trace your way through this maze and add another stripe to this tiger's fur.

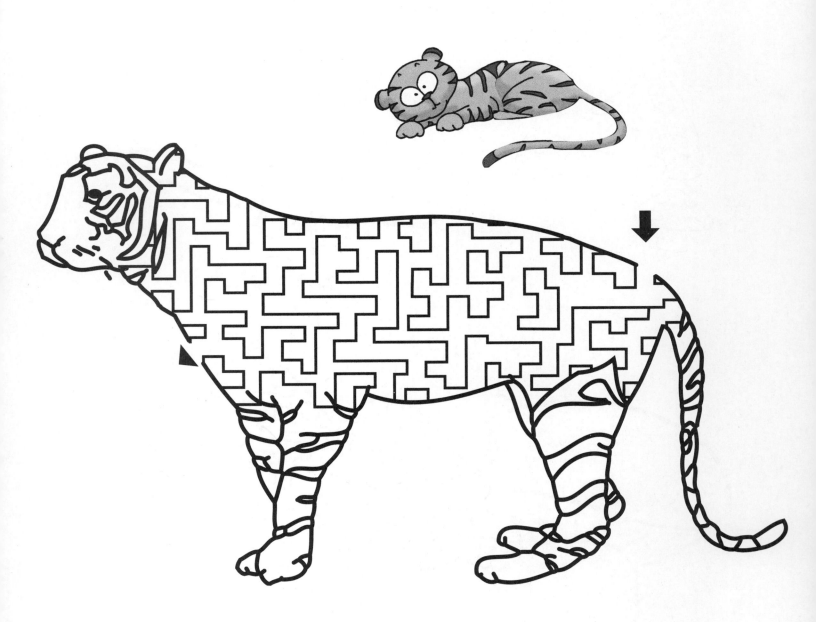

DOG

Trace a line from the dog's eye to his wagging tail.

CAT

Add another stripe to this tabby cat's coat by tracing your way through the maze.

RABBIT

Trace a line from the rabbit's ear to its bobtail.

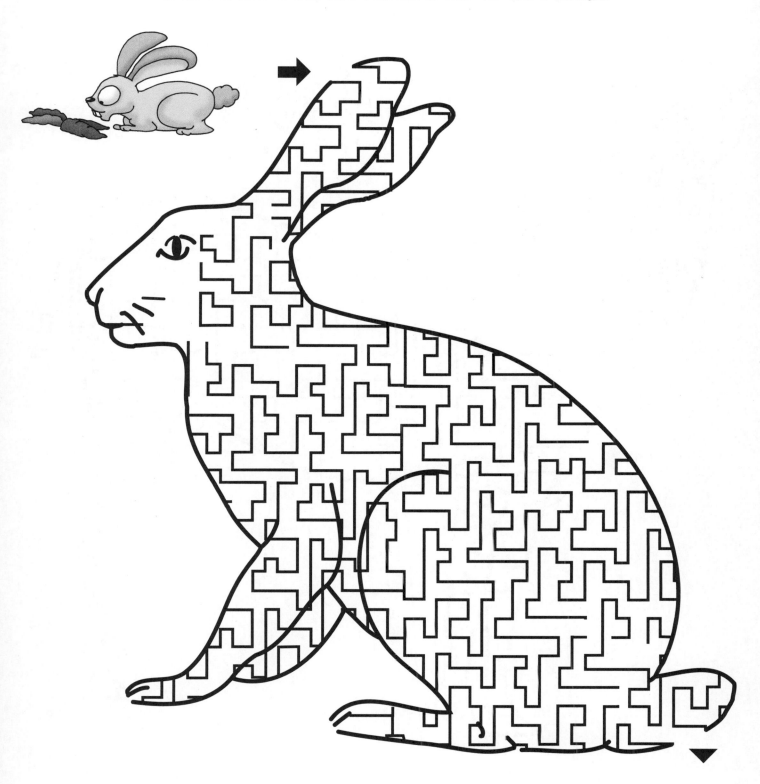

ZEBRA

Trace your way across this magnificent beast to its tail.

MOUSE

Draw a line that connects the mouse's tail to the cheese he is nibbling.

BUTTERFLY

Trace across the butterfly to create a pattern on its wings.

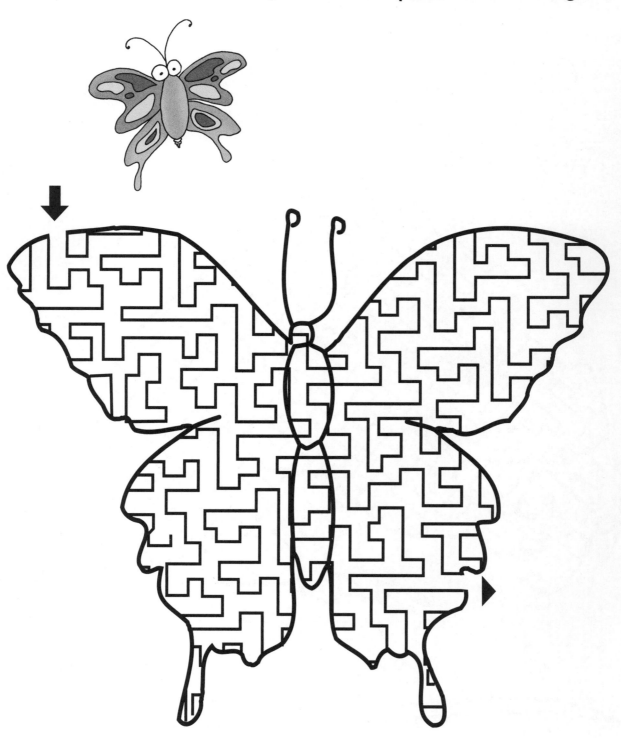

GORILLA

Draw a line up one of the gorilla's arms and down the other.

MONKEY

Trace a line from the monkey's cheeky grin to his curly tail.

HIPPO

Starting and finishing at the hippo's eye, trace a big round shape on the side of his body.

ELEPHANT

Make a line all the way from trunk to tail.

KANGAROO

Draw a line that stretches from the tip of the kangaroo's tail into her pouch.

CAMEL

Make your way across this camel's a-maze-ing saddle.

REINDEER

Draw a line from the tip of one of the reindeer's huge antlers to the other.

WATER BUFFALO

Trace a line from the buffalo's ear to the little bird on his back.

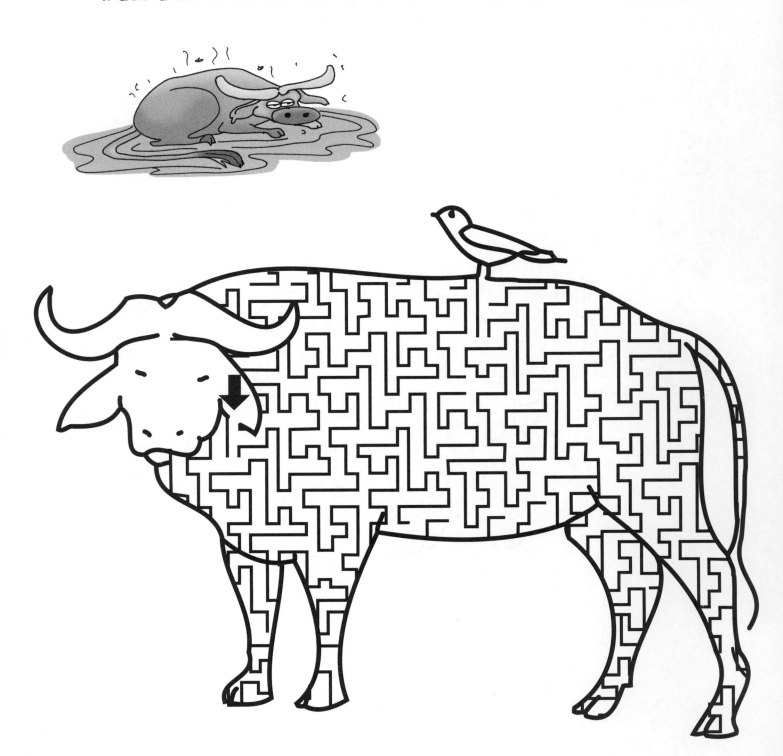

GOAT

Trace a line from the goat's horn to his tail.

PIG

Starting and finishing at the pig's eye, trace
a big round shape on the side of his body.

OSTRICH

Make your way through the maze from head to tail.

BEAR AND CUB

Connect baby bear's nose to the fish that his mother has caught in her mouth.

FROG

Blaze a trail through this maze and put a pattern on the frog's back.

STARFISH

Can you follow a clear path across this starfish?

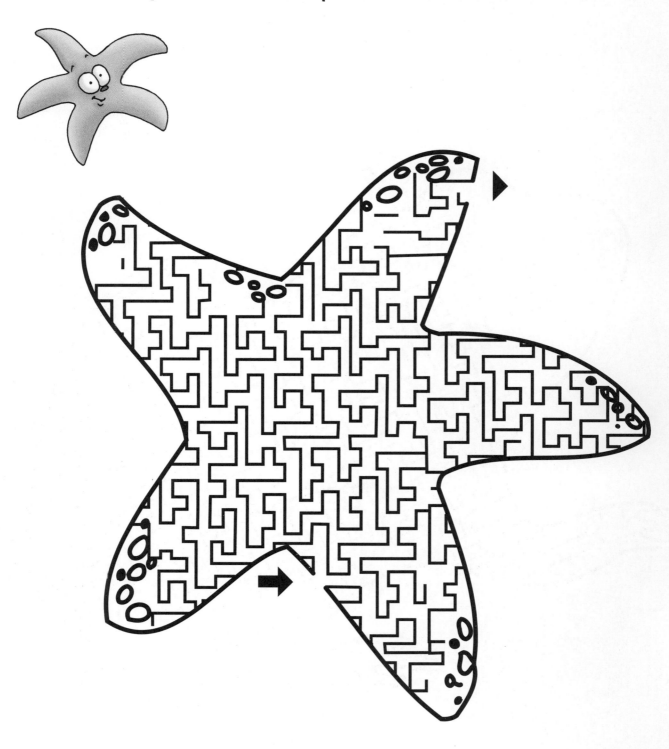

WHALE

Connect the tail of the whale to her waterspout.

SEAHORSE

Trace a line from his nose to his tail.

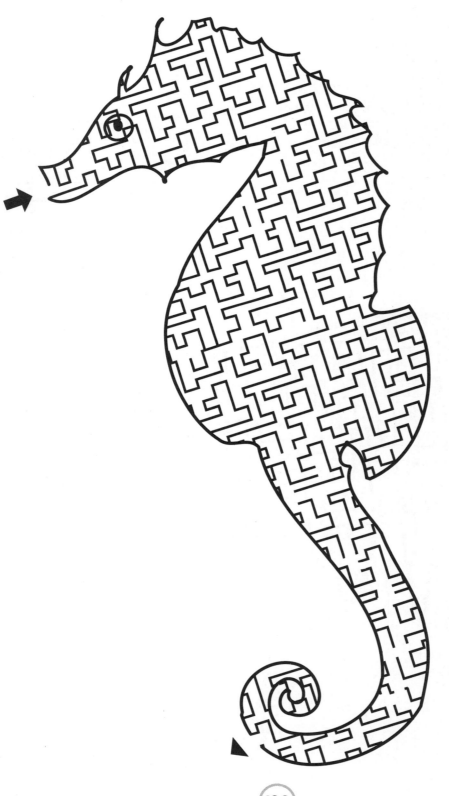

HEXMAZE

Don't get vexed with the hex!

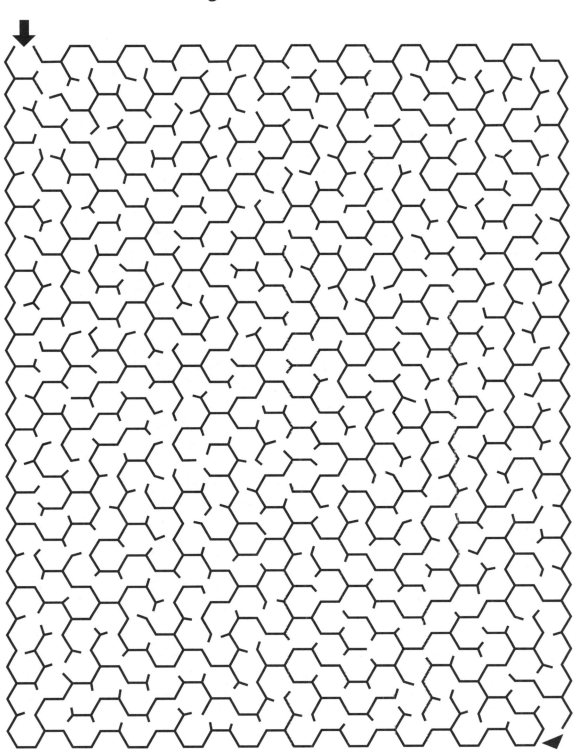

A ROUND DOZEN

Connect the numbers in order. It's as easy as 1 to 12!

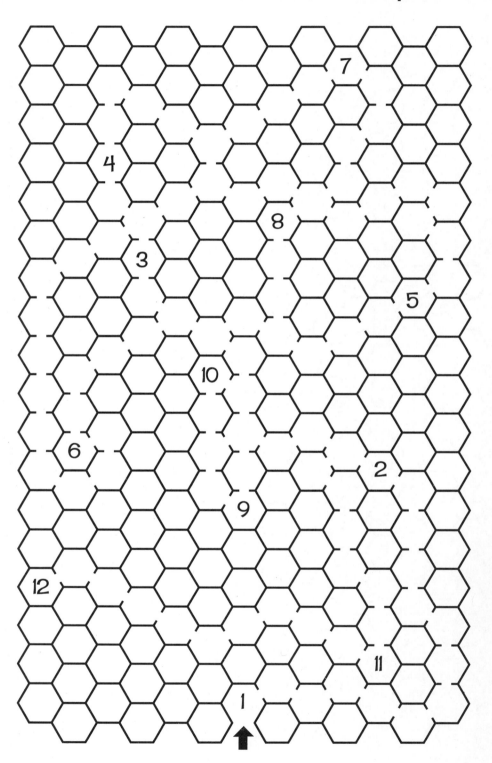

CROSS-COUNTRY SKI

The skier must be careful not to run into any trees on his way to the finish line.

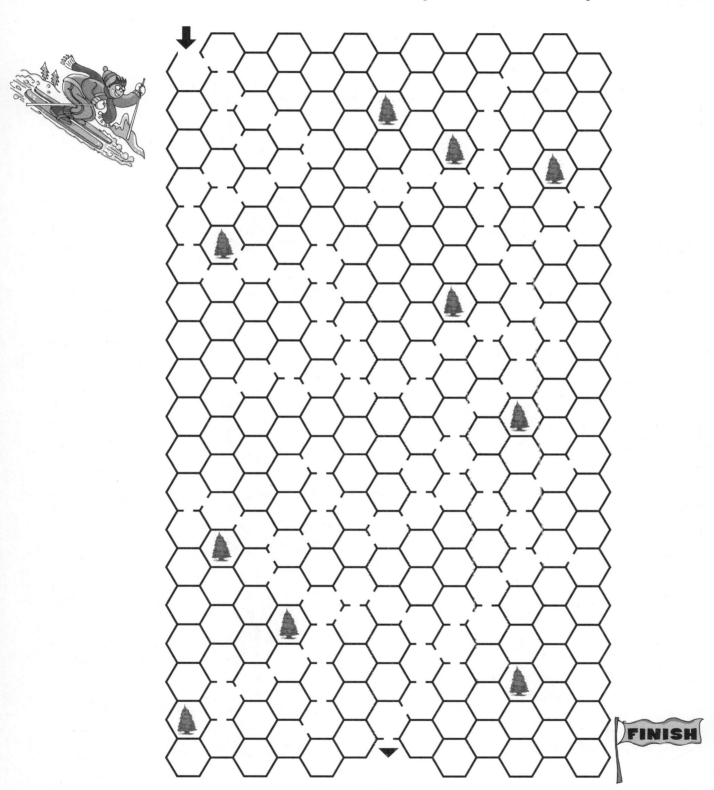

FINISH

HONEYCOMB

Dodge the bees to get at the honey!

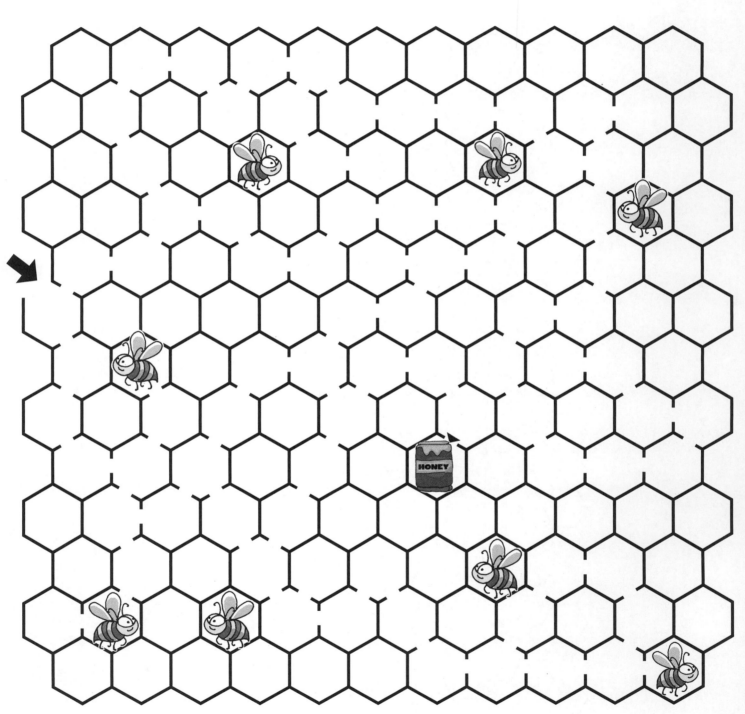

CASTAWAY

Jim's raft is drifting dangerously through shark-infested waters.
Which way does the current take him to the island?

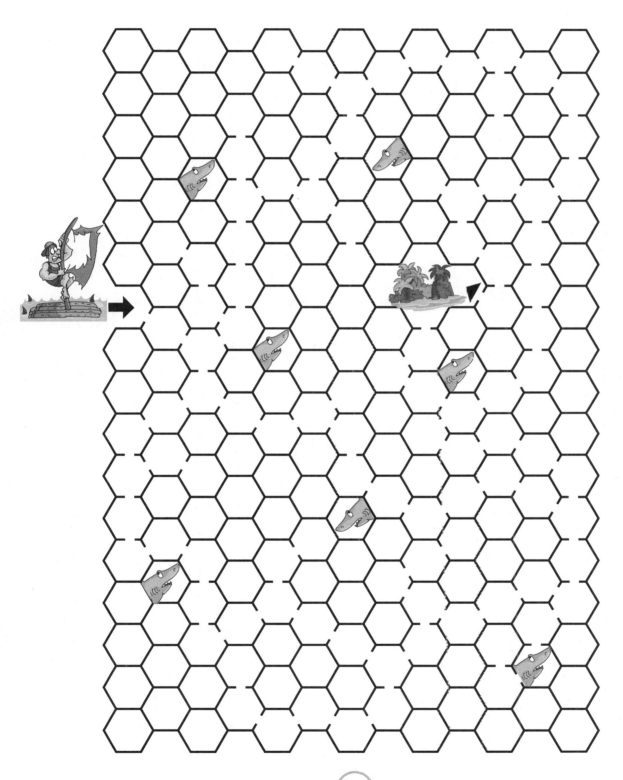

CRISS-CROSS CHALLENGE

Trace one path up and another from side to side.
The cross marks the only place where they intersect.

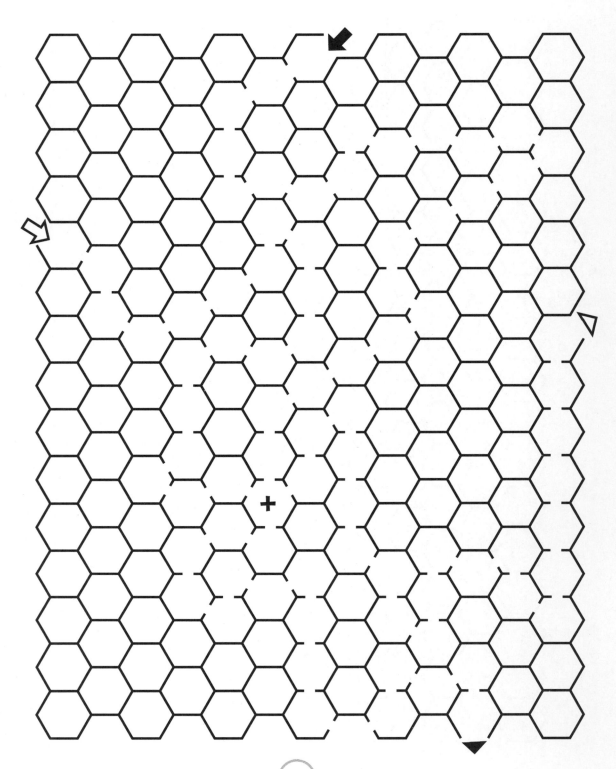

MOTOR MAZE

Drive without a stop from start to finish.

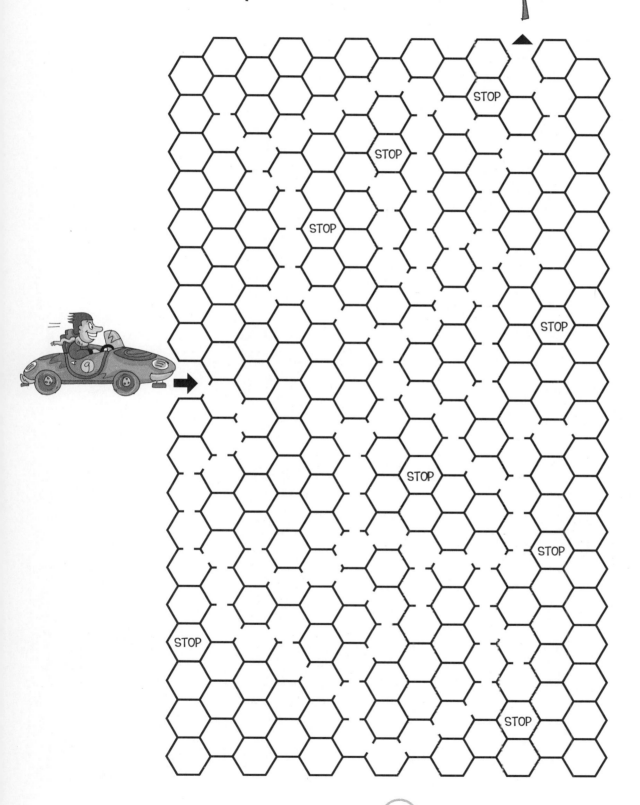

SPOOKY SPECS

All eyes are upon you as you search for the exit.

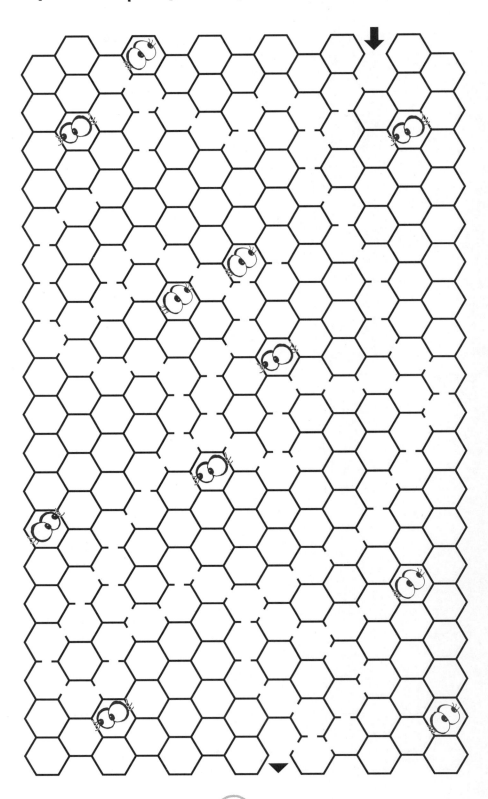

DODGING THE SHOWERS

Dodge the raindrops as you hurry for shelter.

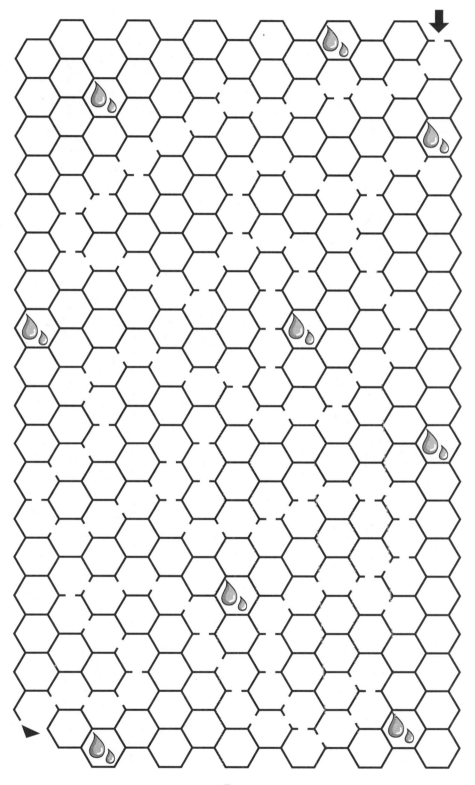

ROSE GARDEN

Make your way around the garden, admiring the roses as you go.

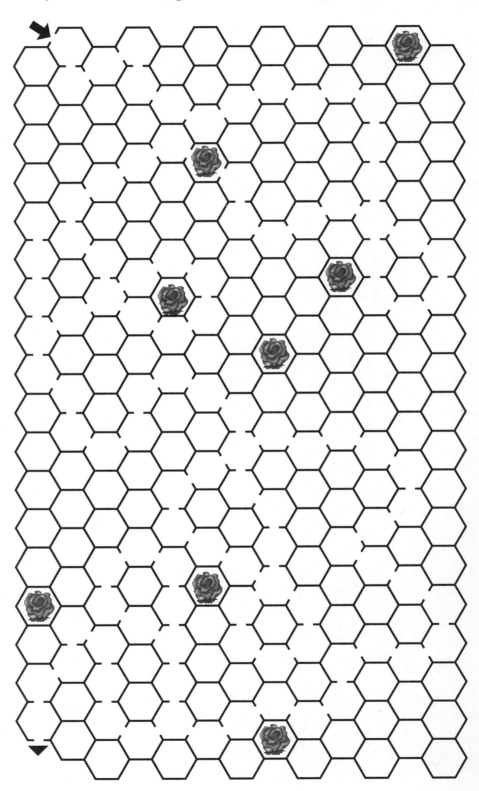

FOOTSTEPS IN THE FOG

You wander in the fog for hours, hearing footsteps behind you, bumping into people, until at last you find your way home.

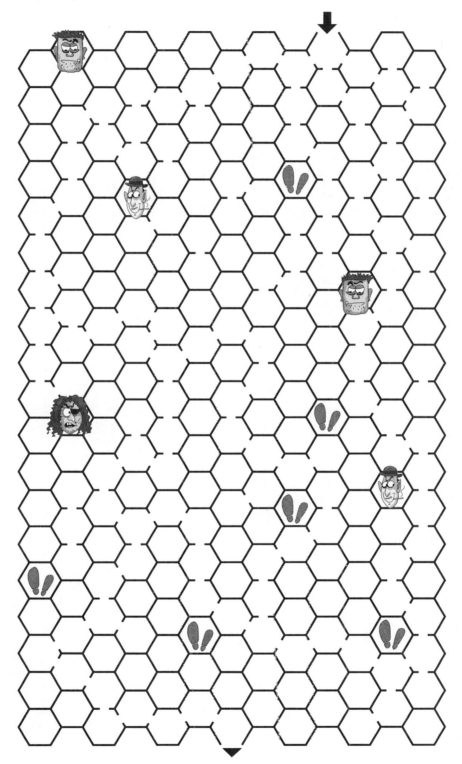

SOLUTIONS

Puzzle Mazes

Page 4

Page 5

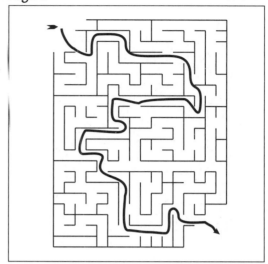

Page 6

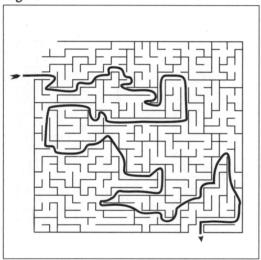

Page 7

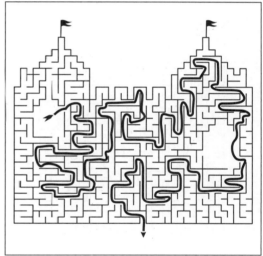

Page 8

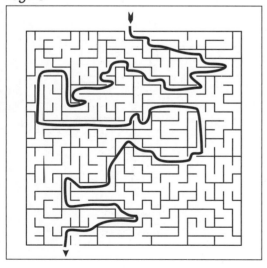

Page 9

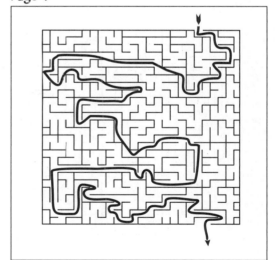

Page 10

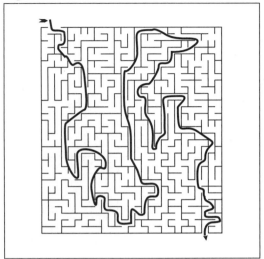

Page 11

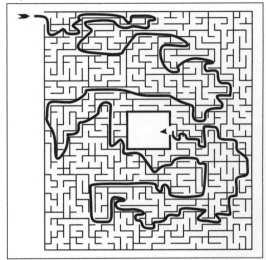

Page 12

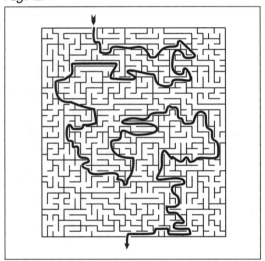

Page 13

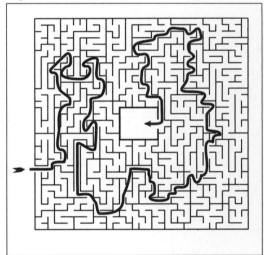

Page 14

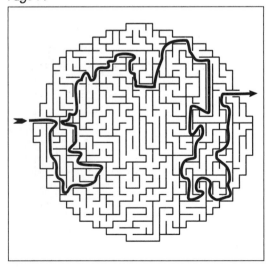

Page 15

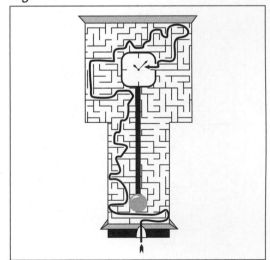

Page 16

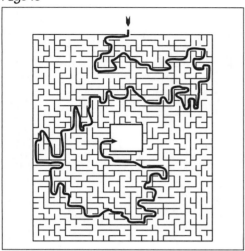

Page 17

Page 18

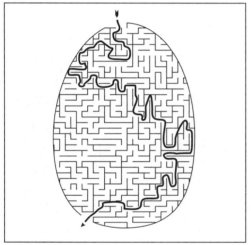

Page 19

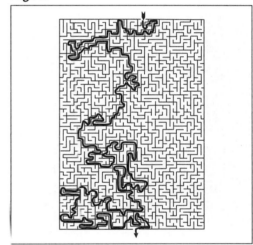

Page 20

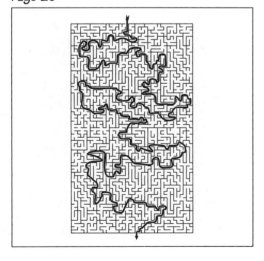

Page 21

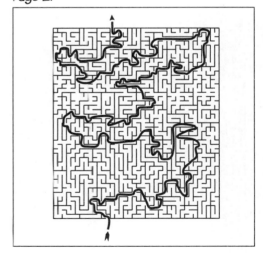

Page 22

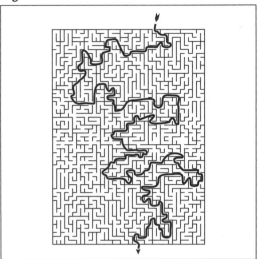

Page 23

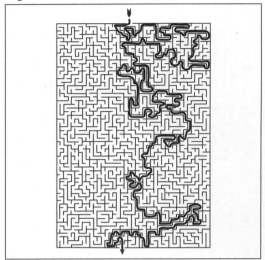

Page 24

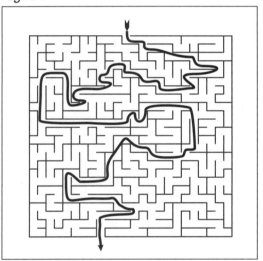

Page 25

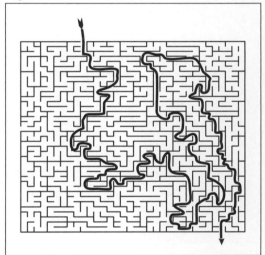

Page 26

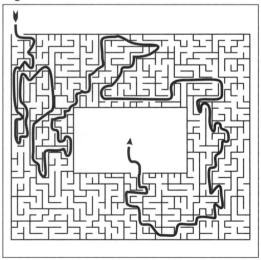

Page 27

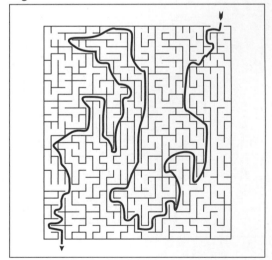

Page 28

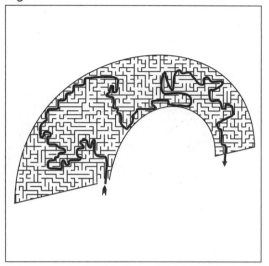

Page 29

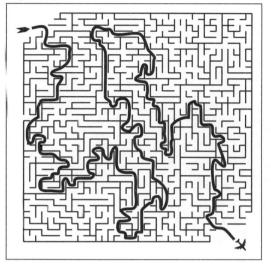

Page 30

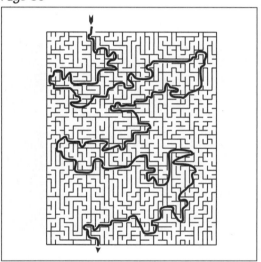

Page 31

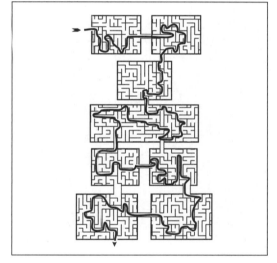

Page 32

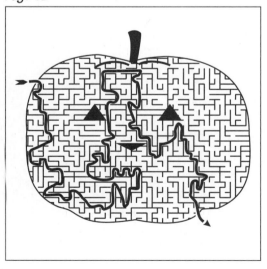

Page 33

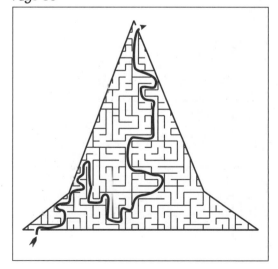

Page 34

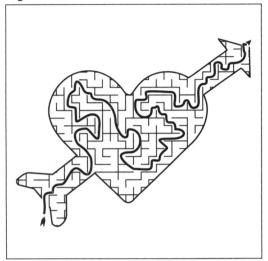

Page 35

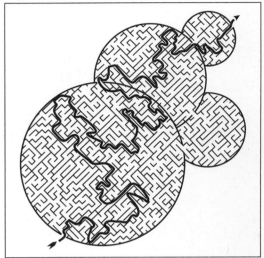

Page 36

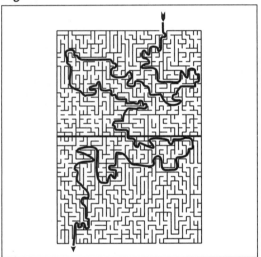

Page 37

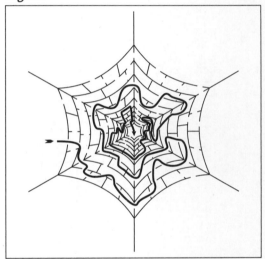

Page 38

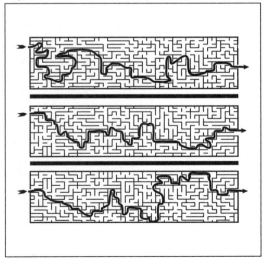

Page 39

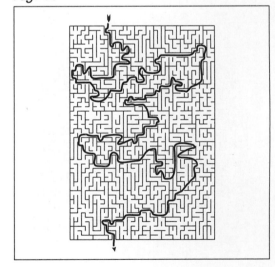

Page 40

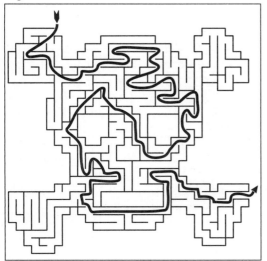

Page 41

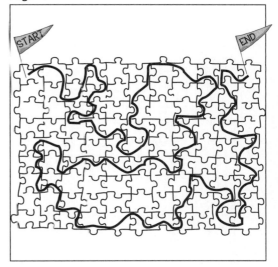

Page 42

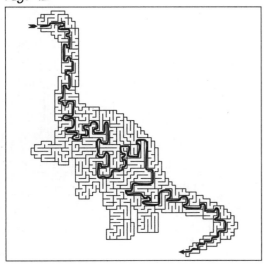

Page 43

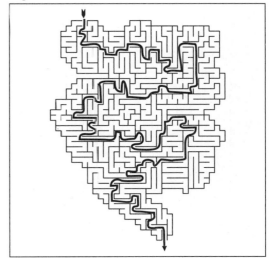

Page 44

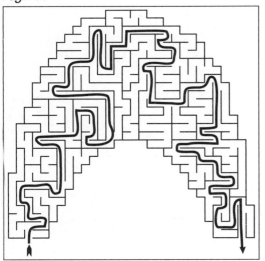

Page 45

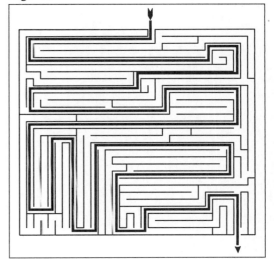

Page 46

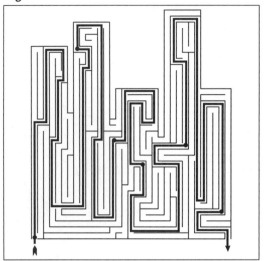

Page 47

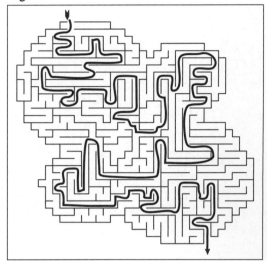

Page 48

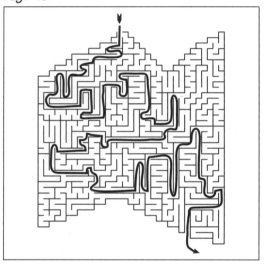

Page 49

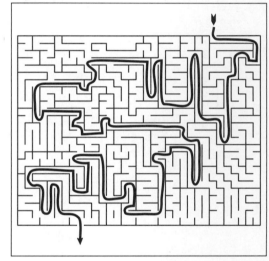

Page 50

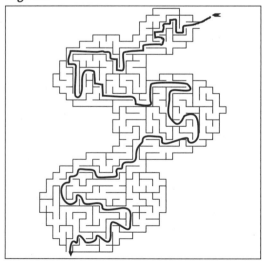

Page 51

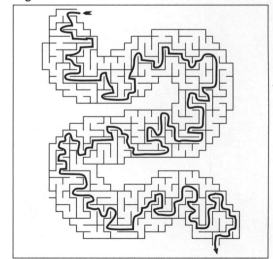

Page 52

Page 53

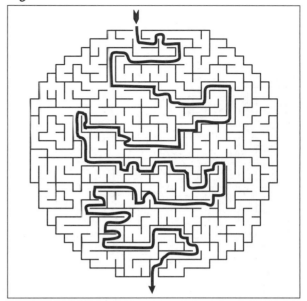

Page 54

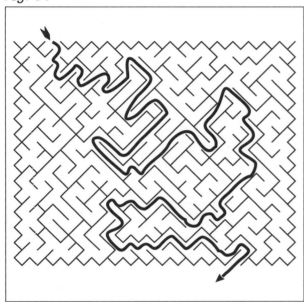

Page 55

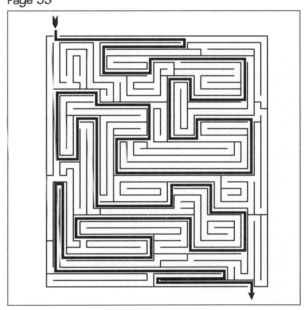

Page 56

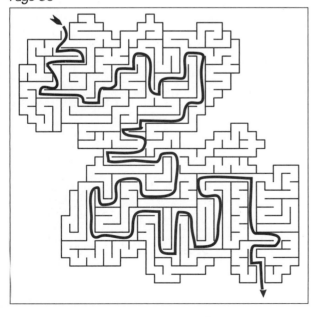

Page 57

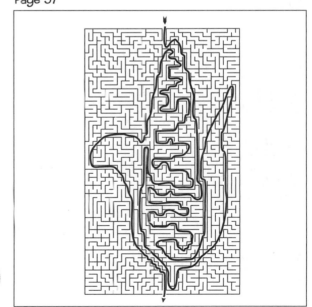

Page 58

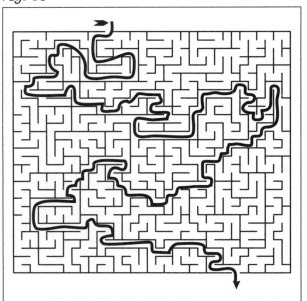

Page 59

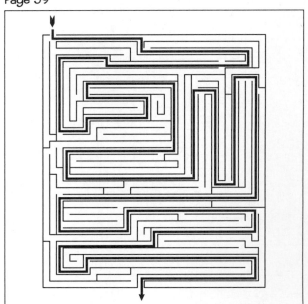

Classic Labyrinth Mazes

Page 60

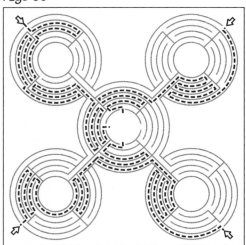

Page 61

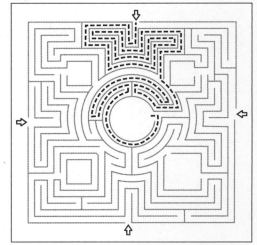

Page 62

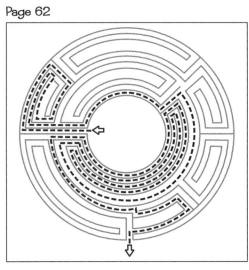

Page 63

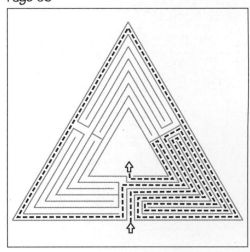

Page 64

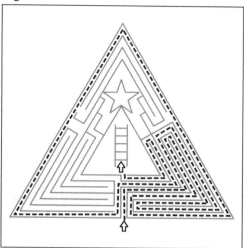

Page 65

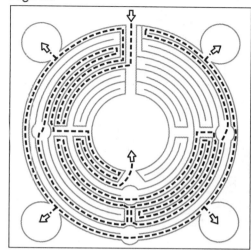

Page 66

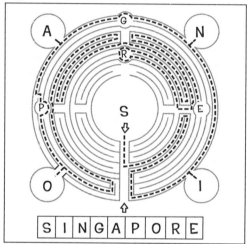

SINGAPORE

Page 67

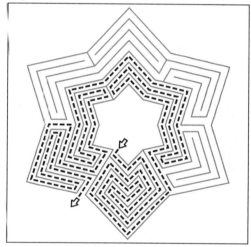

Page 68

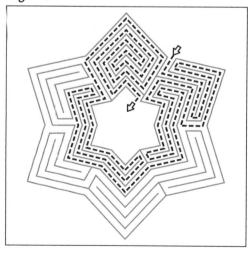

Page 69

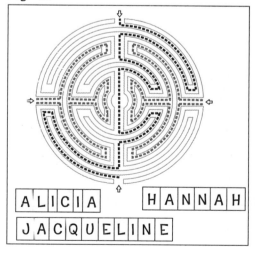

ALICIA   HANNAH

JACQUELINE

Page 70

ROGER   DAVID
ALESSANDRO

Page 71

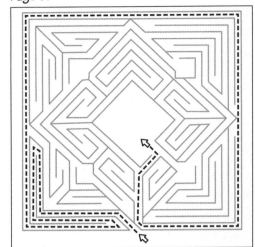

Page 72

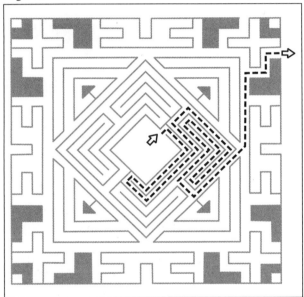

Page 73

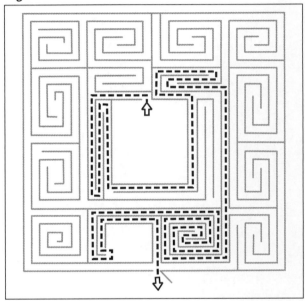

Page 74

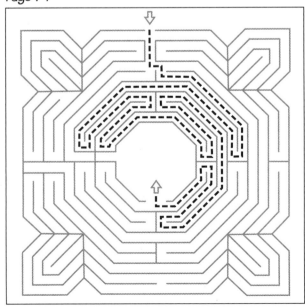

Page 75

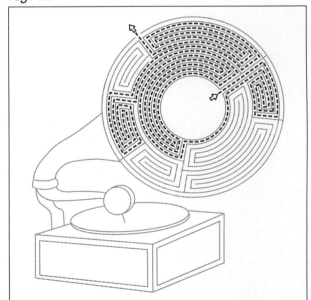

Page 76

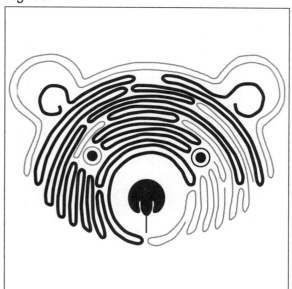

Page 77

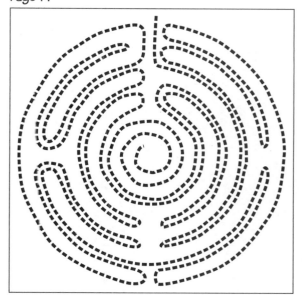

Page 78

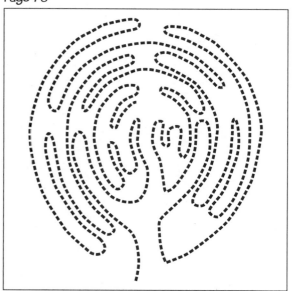

Page 79

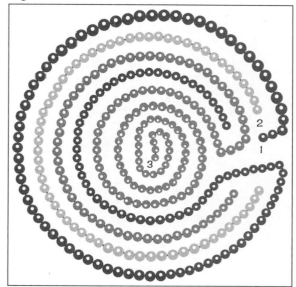

Tangle Mazes

Page 80

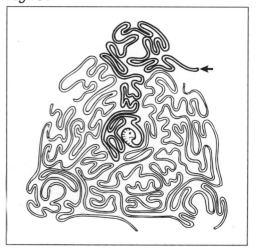

Page 81

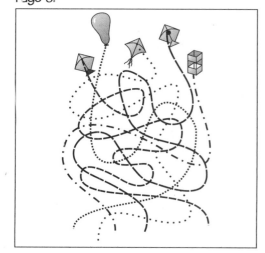

Page 82

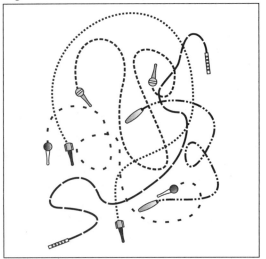

Page 83

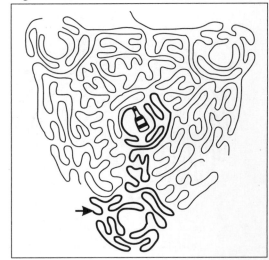

Page 84

Page 85

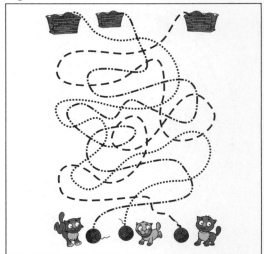

Page 86

Page 87

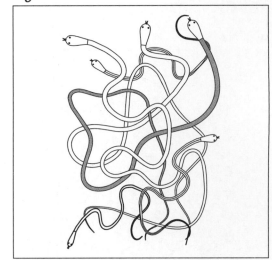

Page 88

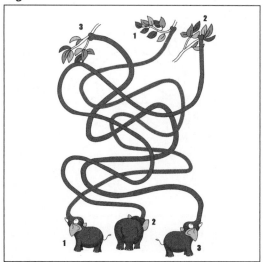

Page 89

Page 90

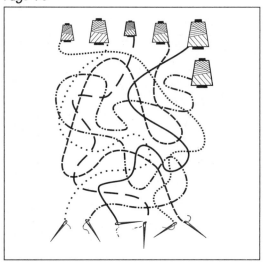

Page 91

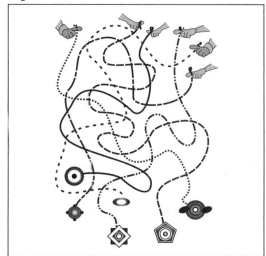

Page 92

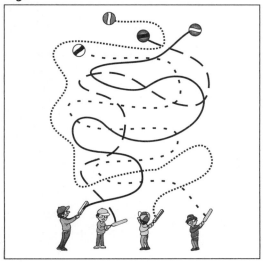

Page 93

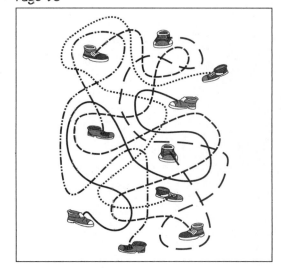

Page 94

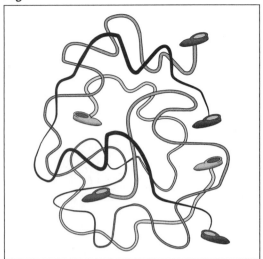

Page 95

Page 96

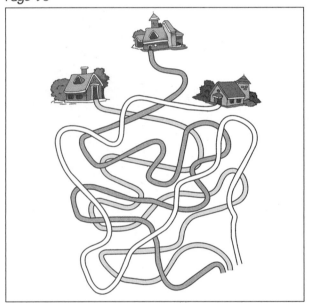

Page 97

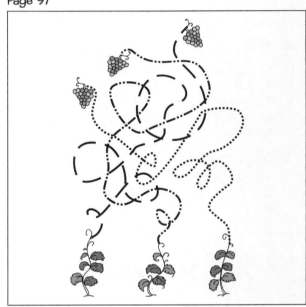

Page 98

Fractal Mazes

Page 99

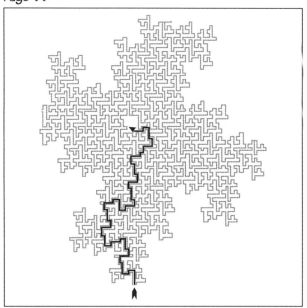

Page 100

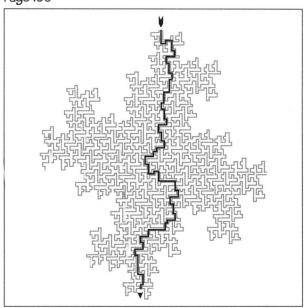

Page 101

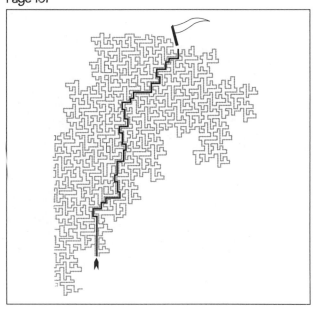

Page 102

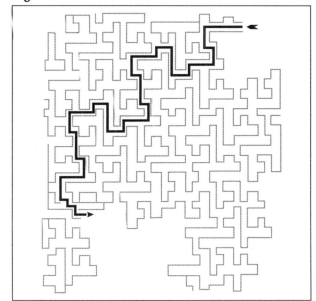

Page 103

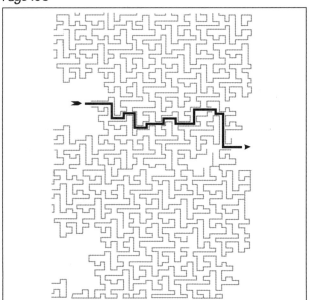

Page 104

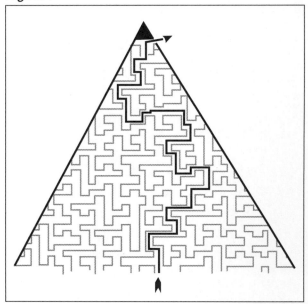

Page 105

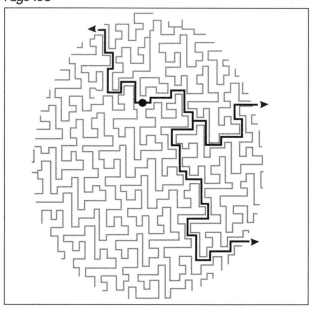

Page 106

Page 107

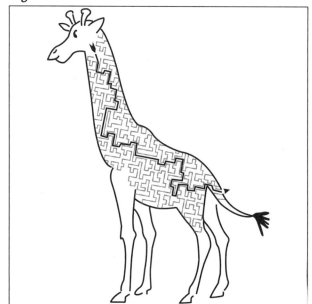

Page 108

Page 109

Page 110

Page 111

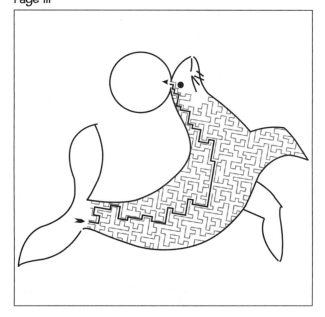

Page 112

Page 113

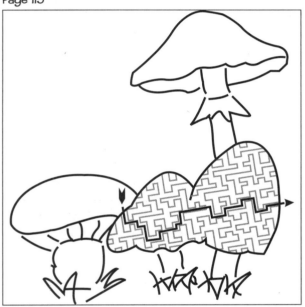

Page 114

Page 115

Page 116

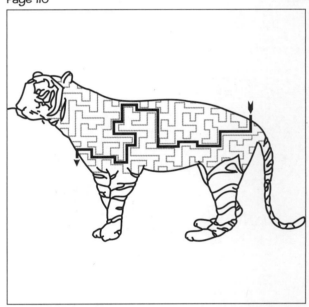

Page 117

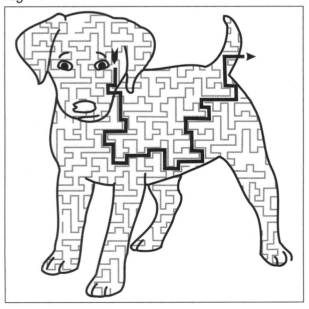

Page 118

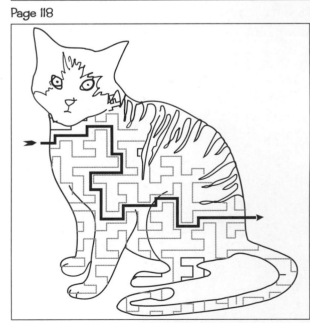

Page 119

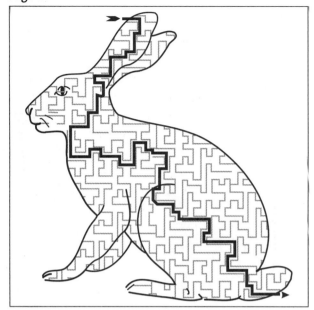

Page 120

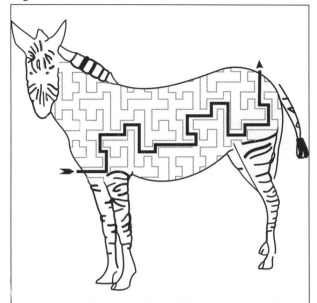

Page 121

Page 122

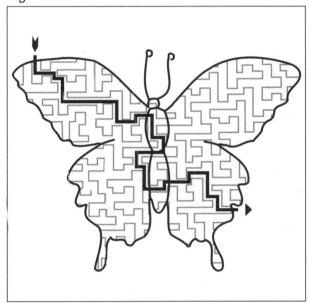

Page 123

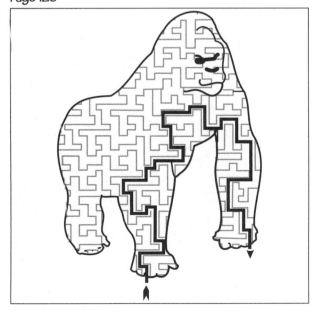

Page 124

Page 125

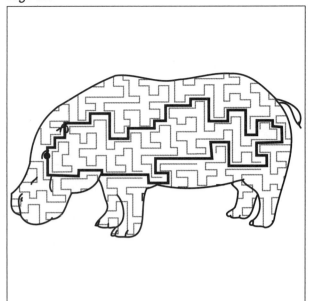

Page 126

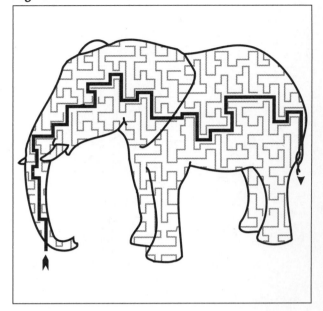

Page 127

Page 128

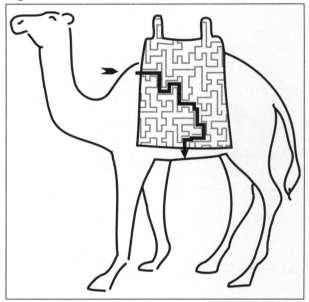

Page 129

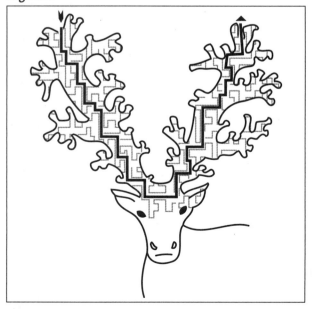

Page 130

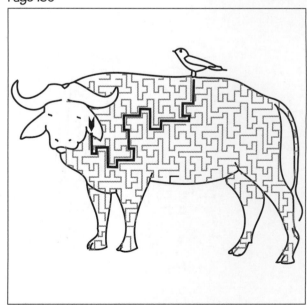

Page 131

Page 132

Page 133

Page 134

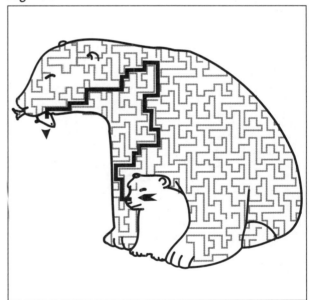

Page 135

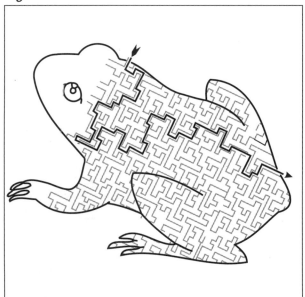

Page 136

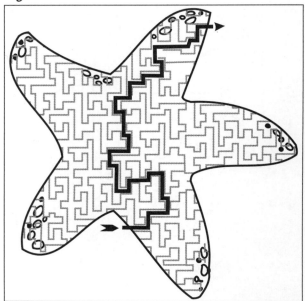

Page 137

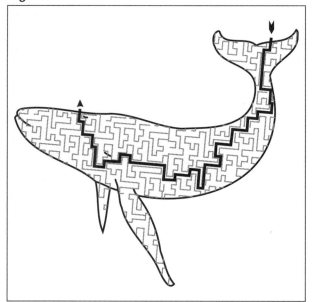

Page 138

Hexagon Mazes

Page 139

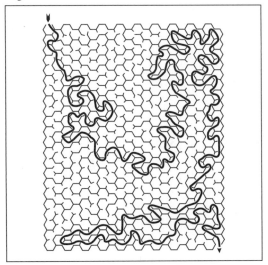

Page 140

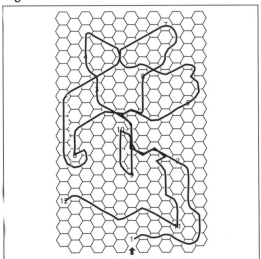

Page 141

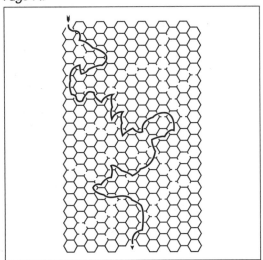

Page 142

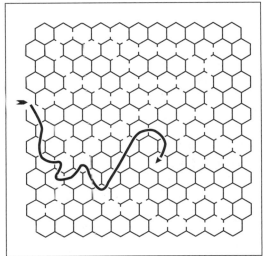

Page 143

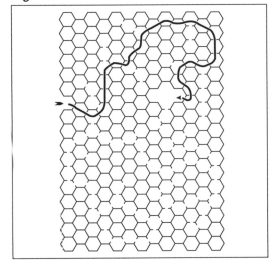

Page 144

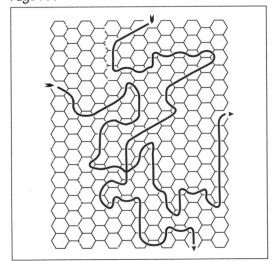

Page 145

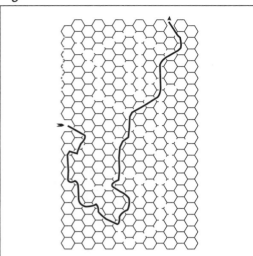

Page 146

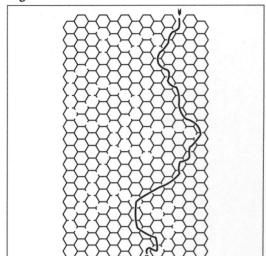

Page 147

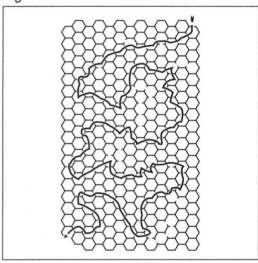

Page 148

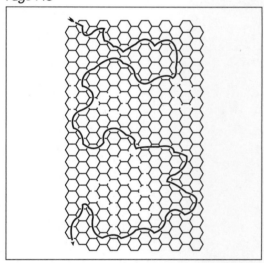

Page 149

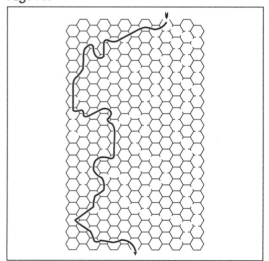